Dan Hyland
Police Reporter

★★★★★★★★★★★★★★★★★★★★★★★★★★★★★★★★

Dan Hyland
Police Reporter

By

NORTON HUGHES JONATHAN

The
Goldsmith Publishing Company
CHICAGO

★★★★★★★★★★★★★★★★★★★★★★★★★★★★★★★★

FOR

RICHARD DOUGLAS JONATHAN
*...For him, the best of
everything—always.*

"There's a place at the top of the ladder for the fellow playing the game of Life according to the rules—hard and clean."

—From Dan Hyland's Notebook

CONTENTS

CONTENTS—*Concluded*

DAN HYLAND, POLICE REPORTER

CHAPTER I

Through the Storm

"SO you want to be a reporter!"

Those words, snapped at him by George Anderson Gargan, the famous managing editor, had challenged young Dan Hyland—had started him on his career as an ace police reporter.

Dan had left school early, after his second college year. His uncle, Ray Hyland, a famous newspaper man now writing for the Hollywood motion picture companies, had sent Dan to Gargan.

"I suppose you edited your school paper," Gargan had grunted as Dan faced him for the first time, armed with a letter of introduction.

"No sir," Dan replied. "I didn't even try out for the staff. I earned my way through two years of college and didn't have time for extra activities."

"Well, at least you are different from the rest
of the bright young men who pester me for reporting jobs. Your uncle thinks you've got the
makings of a real newspaper man. I'll soon know!
I'm going to assign you to police work in the
toughest ward in Chicago. From now on you'll
wear a press pass in your hat band and chase
squad cars."

And so Dan Hyland had begun as a cub police
reporter, riding with the night cruisers, covering
the night court, and watching the work of great
detectives. His rise on the Chicago Daily Star
from a cub to the ace police reporter and feature
writer of the staff was rapid, almost sensational—
the typical rise of a born "newshawk" who hears
the rumble of mighty presses in the dead of the
night when all the world is calm and still. The
faith of Ray Hyland and the generosity of
George Anderson Gargan were amply rewarded.

Dan knew Chicago's underworld well. Secretly he had gathered damaging evidence
against Jules Sparoni, notorious gang leader. His
detective work took him to St. Louis and southern Illinois—and now he was flying back to Chicago through a bad storm with the great story
he had risked his life to obtain.

The storm ruled the night. Long flashes of
jagged, claw-like lightning flared at short inter-

vals, lighting up sky and earth with a silver brilliance. Through the perils of the storm-swept darkness Dan Hyland flew his monoplane at its best speed, unmindful of the grim danger confronting him each second, his thoughts centered on the leather manuscript case beside him in the cockpit. Driving rain slashed his face; the wind, rapidly reaching gale proportions, screamed a song of warning through the thick helmet protecting his head and ears.

Below the scudding plane, the ground seemed to heave and toss like a crazy thing as the monoplane responded to Dan Hyland's sure touch and roared on through the night—twisting, rolling, zooming to tear loose from the determined claws of the storm.

The young pilot strained his eyes for a glimpse of the ground as a snake-like flash of lightning, more brilliant than those before it, turned night into day for an all too brief instant. He could make out nothing but gray sheets of pelting, swirling wet. He was alone in the sky with death lurking ahead in the endless void before the whirling propeller blades.

There could be no turning back now. He must fly on—on through wind and rain until the lights of the Chicago airport blinked below, advertising a welcome refuge. The manuscript case beside him must be in the hands of the Chicago Star's managing editor before dawn. He kept that one thought in his mind constantly. Important papers were in that case—papers which would mean victory for the Chicago Star in its fight for honest government in the great city on Lake Michigan.

Dan fought to climb above the rain. Now it was growing colder, and cold would mean a losing battle against leaden sleet formations on the wings of the ship. Fat orange flames streaked from its exhaust. The pattern of spitting fire climbed higher, was lost for a moment, and then magically appeared once more as the lightning framed the silver of the monoplane against dark, angry storm clouds. Dan's fleet air steed was a ghost—a restless spirit roaring steadily onward toward Chicago and safety.

For the next fifteen minutes he had only the thundering motor and gleaming cockpit instruments for company. He was alone in a sea of stinging rain and blackness, fighting for a glimpse of a landing beacon, striving to pierce the emptiness with keen eyes. But the secretive storm clutched him in angry wet fingers and refused him a glimpse of the ground.

According to the delicate instruments before him, he was directly over his destination. Dan glanced at the illuminated panel, as if to reassure himself, and then made a daring decision. He resolved to plunge earthward, to drop dizzily through the storm, so it would be possible for him to locate the airport.

The monoplane spun like a top and flung itself downward like a falling rocket. The dive was a breath-taking stunt which hurled the young aviator through the worst of the storm area in danger-filled seconds. The snarling gale tried to toss him toward the hidden stars as the monoplane struck a strong up current of air, but the flailing "prop" blades knifed through the eddy, shot him toward the ground.

It was better going now. The sobbing wail of the wind droned in his ears as he cut the plane's pounding motor. He must not dive too far, and now his altimeter warned against further descent.

Suddenly there came a silent warning. Something unknown asserted itself and shouted to him that the ground was dangerously near—far too close for comfort. He had whipped out of the storm and into the somewhat lighter strata of fog and rain embracing the earth. In a flash the Daily Star's flying reporter saw Chicago spread out like a huge, jagged carpet below him. The city was weirdly luminous as it lay sleeping in foggy shroud-like atmosphere.

Dan gained his correct bearing quickly. A brief survey told him that he was only a mile away from the municipal air field. Hours spent in the clouds above the city and in its streets had photographed it upon his memory.

He flew low, his motor no doubt alarming those few on the streets on that dreary Tuesday early morning. Wiping the rain from his goggles, he watched for the airport's beacon and it was not long before his vigilance was rewarded. Security was near! Then a truant flash of lightning revealed a hard packed field. Landing lights dotted the mist below him.

Dan leaned out and noted the position of the runway marker lamps and swiftly prepared to land. All was clear on the ground, and his wailing motor advertised his arrival to the landing crew on duty. More lights were switched on; floodlamps glowed.

Dan Hyland circled the field and roared over the huge commercial hangars, then expertly tilted his plane downward. Dark water, rippling on the surface of packed earth, rushed up to meet him, and a moment later his landing wheels touched the ground. The monoplane landed perfectly but wabbled as it ploughed through mud and water.

Dan rolled across the landing field and into

the dim shadows cast by the Chicago Star's own private hangar. There would be a car waiting there to carry him to the Daily Star building. The hangar floodlights were turned on as the plane was recognized.

Soaked to the skin, Dan asked only for the chance to go at once to his apartment for a hot bath and sleep—hours of it. He had not enjoyed the luxury of a bed for over thirty-six hours. He had been flying almost constantly, interviewing state authorities and known criminals, and he had come back to Chicago and the Star with a sensational exposé which would end once and for all the political domination of Jules Sparoni and his gangsters. In twenty-four hours Sparoni's power would be broken and he and his gang apprehended. Dan had gathered the amazing facts; the Daily Star would print them. The manuscript case contained his great story. A warm sensation of pleasure over his hard won success welled within him as his ship rolled to a stop.

Dan climbed slowly out of the cockpit. Willing hands helped him. He had the precious leather case under one arm.

"Hiyah, Dan! Glad to see you back safe and sound." Reporter Billy Parker's upturned laughing face loomed at Dan's side, a welcome sight to his tired friend. Dan yelled back at him. There was a friendly pounding and back slapping.

"You old heathen! Billy, I'm sure glad to spot your homely face. Let's hurry into town. I'm anxious to hand my big story in and get out to the apartment."

"O.K., Danny. We're practically on our way. I suppose you got your story on Sparoni?"

"I did, Billy. He is all set for jail. Where's your press car? Behind the hangar?"

"Righto." Billy picked up the small suitcase Dan had taken with him on his air jaunt.

They walked around the side of the hangar, skipping over the mud puddles. Three mechanics had taken over the monoplane and were preparing to ease it into its berth. They sloshed on out to where a Star coupé waited. They climbed in, and Billy started the motor and turned on the heater. Dan made himself as comfortable as his soaked clothing would allow.

Morning had not yet fully come to the city. The rain had stopped but a heavy mist remained. The mud spattered lamps of the coupé cast light upon the outlines of oil refineries, factories, and the lines of tank and freight cars standing like beasts of burden on spur tracks beside the highway. The car sped over the drainage canal, its rapidly turning wheels causing a hollow sound as they crossed the bridge.

Now long rows of silent houses stood out in bold relief against the muddy dullness of the sky. Street cars sailed through the fog, like stately lighted ships, and a freight engine on the "Q" railroad chuffed over the Cicero avenue viaduct, its open fire door blotching crimson against the sky. The few people on the street seemed shabby and morose. It is difficult to be gay and buoyant at five o'clock in the morning.

Billy turned the machine into Ogden Avenue, increasing its speed. Something unknown and unexplainable made Dan turn in the seat and peer out of the rear window. Racing through the gloom, directly behind the fast moving newspaper coupé, was a dark limousine. Twin headlamps gleamed dully. Dan knew that pursuing car. It belonged to Jules Sparoni.

Dan's body tensed and his voice was a shout of warning.

"Look out, Billy! We're being followed."

Billy Parker glanced back quickly—his eyes taking in the situation at a glance. The other machine—Sparoni's death limousine—was rapidly overtaking them. Dan was pushing the manuscript case down out of sight and looking out warily.

Billy made an unexpected move. As the limousine shot alongside, he spun his wheel. Tires protesting shrilly, the newspaper car swerved and darted toward the curb. Towering buildings shoved up close walls that shut out the dim light. The limousine's brakes squealed. The ugly snout of a machine gun was thrust from a side window.

"Duck!" Billy yelled the words.

Crouching low in the coupé, they heard the staccato yammering of the death gun. Jules Sparoni was answering the challenge of the Daily Star—answering with singing bullets.

Steel stung into the coupé, the bullets sounding like hailstones on a tin roof. For long seconds the sub-machine gun chattered, spitting livid flame. . . . Then all was still.

"All right, Billy?" Dan whispered hoarsely.

"Sure, I'm all right," the other answered. "They've ruined this suit I'm wearing, though. A slug went through the sleeve of my coat. It didn't even graze me, but it made a big hole in the cloth. I'm glad this car has a steel body. That's what saved us."

"We're not out of danger yet," Dan reminded him grimly.

They lay, cramped and still, on the floorboards. Suddenly they heard heavy footsteps. Someone was coming toward the car. Their motor, idling, throbbed monotonously.

"Play dead, Billy, or we really will be corpses."

They heard the footsteps approach the side of the car and stop. Dan's heart pounded. His body seemed suddenly sheathed in ice. Was this to be the end?

For a moment fear paralyzed him, making his body numb. For the space of a heart beat he could not have moved even though his life depended upon it. Then his will power came to the rescue. Something had to be done, and in a hurry.

Still remaining inert on the floorboards, Dan opened one eye a little and gazed upward. A flat, cruel face was looking in through the window, gazing down at the pair. Dan's brain snapped into action and his muscles responded.

Sharply Dan Hyland ordered, "Raise your hand, you—quickly!" It was a nervy thing to say as he didn't have a gun, but he hoped to startle the gangster. He succeeded.

The man's head snapped back through the window opening. A flashing movement answered Dan's order—a hand darting holsterward. Dan sprang upward, like an uncoiling spring, in a single swift motion. He heard Billy struggling up beside him. A gun glittered in the dashboard light. Dan threw his body forward. Twice the weapon spat. Wood splintered beside Billy

Parker. Dan aimed a lightning blow, feeling the slugs rip through his clothing, and struck with all his weight behind the blow.

His hard fist pounded into the flat face of the man with the gun. The man grunted. His shadow-like figure went rigid and toppled to the pavement like an unbalanced statue.

Dan yelled an order.

"Billy—cripple their car! Back into it!"

Billy Parker did as he was ordered. Racing the motor, he shot the press car into reverse. It jerked backward, plunging into the limousine. There was a shout and a loud crash as steel smashed into steel. The death car's right front wheel crumpled.

"We've got them! Now, step on it."

Billy hastily shifted gears and the coupé lunged ahead, accelerating to high speed. They rocked into an alley, tires howling and volleyed down its length. The coupé pitched through the gloom.

"Ride your horn and keep the gas pedal down to the floorboard."

Billy and Dan were again on their way to the offices of the Chicago Daily Star.

CHAPTER II

The Lion's Den

DAN HYLAND, closely followed by Billy Parker, stepped from the Star building elevator at the sixth floor and entered the noise and confusion of the city news room.

Typewriter keys pounded under shaded green lamps. Copy boys hurried up and down crowded, waste paper strewn aisles. Shirt sleeved men bent over battered desks. The entire staff was working at top speed to get out the first of the morning final editions.

Dan crossed from the doorway to the city desk in a few quick strides. Billy Parker fell behind him and stopped at his own typewriter. Fellow reporters shouted words of greeting and congratulations and Dan yelled back as he dumped his manuscript onto the City Editor's desk.

"All here?" City editor Andy Blayne had zipped open the case and was rapidly leafing through the sheets of copy paper, eagerly reading the important story Dan had typed in a St. Louis hotel room.

"Sure, Andy. It's the works. My story is there and also the proof backing me up—the confessions I obtained from ex-members of Sparoni's gang."

"Fine work, Dan, I'll get in touch with the Department of Justice and turn this evidence you've collected over to them. They'll nab Sparoni and his men before noon."

"Tell the G-men to look for him on the west side," Dan advised. "Billy and I just saw something of Jules. In fact, I saw a little too much of him, and he gave me something to remember him by."

Dan exhibited the bullet holes in his coat. Andy Blayne looked at them and whistled softly.

The managing editor's pretty secretary, Ashley Church, stopped in surprise beside Andy Blayne's horseshoe shaped desk. She started suddenly when she saw the young flying reporter.

"Oh, it's you, Dan," she said in a startled voice. "I wasn't quite sure for a moment. You're as pale as a ghost."

Dan smilingly showed her the bullet holes. "I almost became one. Fortunately for Billy and me, Sparoni's gunmen aren't very good shots."

"When does Gargan want to see Dan?" Andy Blayne asked the girl.

"Right away. Now."

Five minutes later Dan faced the managing editor across the great desk which Gargan used as a barricade. Visitors and Daily Star workers always sat on the other side of that invincible wall.

George Anderson Gargan, known to the staff as "the old man," shifted the black cigar which constantly jutted from his mouth like a jaunty flagpole. Dan thought he saw approval in the famous editor's eyes, but wasn't sure. Gargan was an unsolved puzzle to everyone.

"Go home and get some sleep," Gargan ordered gruffly. "That's all. You can go now."

Dan unfolded his legs and got up. He was a little disappointed. He knew he had done well and expected a word of praise. Solemnly he moved toward the door.

Gargan stopped him with a word. "By the way, Dan—you did pretty well on the Sparoni assignment—and the Star will buy you a new coat. Now get out of here."

As Dan closed the private office door, he thought he heard a sound suspiciously like low, guarded laughter. Old Gargan might be half human after all, he reflected.

Dan shared an apartment in quiet, suburban Riverside with Billy Parker. Riverside was an ideal town with shaded lawns and big, rambling homes. A twenty minute train ride took them to and from the Daily Star building.

At eight o'clock on the morning of his rather damp but completely triumphant return, Dan Hyland prepared for the welcome comfort of his bed and hours of sleep. In pajamas and dressing gown, he surveyed a dripping Riverside from the Link Manor apartments.

Below his window Chicago office workers hurried toward the C. B. & Q. station and the imminent arrival of the 8:06. Funny work—the newspaper game, he reflected, not without amusement. A fellow went to bed when the rest of the world was getting up. Then he went to work when everyone else was thinking of retiring.

He left the windows, stepping through a doorway into his own room. The apartment contained three bedrooms, a living room, and a kitchenette. His own room was neat and carefully arranged.

He crawled delightedly between the cool sheets of his bed. This was great—worth waiting days for! He decided that he did not want to get up again; he never wanted to fight again for an exclusive story. He wanted to lie forever wrapped in the comforting sheets. He was tired— so tired.

In less than three minutes he dropped off to sleep, floating easily away from the reality of his bedroom into a land where George Anderson Gargan assumed the alarming proportions of a King Kong and pursued him over an amazing pink map of the state of Illinois.

Dan had not seen a special delivery letter which Billy Parker had placed on the table beside his bed. The letter was postmarked HOLLYWOOD, CALIFORNIA, and looked important.

Dan smiled and stirred in his sleep. It was as if he realized in his dreams that there were dangerous new adventures ahead for him.

CHAPTER III

Great Opportunity

DAN HYLAND restlessly rolled over in bed and stared with a startled expression at the small electric clock purring on the table at his elbow. He rubbed skeptical eyes. A second glance confirmed the first. It was seven o'clock. He had slept for eleven hours— almost around the clock, and he was still sleepy.

The young police reporter sat up in bed and yawned, after which he felt a little more like his usual self. He switched on the small reading lamp suspended like a bell above his head. As he kicked his way out of the covers, the tinted lamplight brought into sharp outline the strong, regular features of his pleasant, not unhandsome, face—the square, determined young jaw, and the well-knit, powerful healthy body which had made it possible for him to star in football and track during his school days.

Billy Parker bounced into the bedroom like a prizefighter coming out of his corner at the first clang of the timekeeper's gong, and he snapped on the overhead light as he came. Billy was loudly attired in what the well dressed young Chicago reporter will wear if not carefully watched with an untiring eye. Billy's greeting, shouted happily, was a noisy one.

"Hi, son. How's the young reporter?"

"Still sleepy."

"That's funny."

"Why?" Dan was curious in an aimless way.

"Because you've been dead all day. I came in at ten this morning. You were snoring then."

"I can stand days of sleep," Dan informed him. "From now on I can't get enough—can't catch up. Understand?"

"Perfectly."

Dan hugged his knees. "I don't know why I woke up at such a convenient hour of the evening—just in time to go to work. Slave all night; snore all day. That's the reporter's life."

"Gargan doesn't expect you to report for an assignment tonight. You can roll over and fly back to dreamland."

"Well, the old war horse is in for a surprise," Dan announced. "I'm thoroughly awake now. I might as well report as usual tonight. We'll go downtown together on the next train. Might just as well get back into the harness."

Billy Parker now lolled indolently on the foot of the bed, lazy and comfortable.

"What woke you up?" he asked.

"Force of habit, I suppose. I'm used to starting off for work at this hour, you know."

"That's right."

"Aren't you going out on a feature assignment?"

"Yes, I am. But I thought I'd stay here for awhile—until you showed signs of waking. You'd starve to death without little Billy around to cook the potatoes and flop the flap-jacks. If he wakes, I reasoned, he'll want food. I'll get you something to eat and then we'll leave here together."

Dan shifted to another subject. "How long have you been home?"

"Since noon."

"Why so late?"

"Gargan sent me out on a feature assignment. I didn't return to the Star building until eleven o'clock."

"Speaking of the Star—how did my big story go over?"

". . . Like a tank going over the top and through a concrete wall. Sparoni and his entire gang are now behind the bars. The G men rounded them all up this morning, before they had a chance to leave Chicago. Your story was all the evidence the Federals needed. Incidentally, you're quite a hero down at the office. Your good work and daring put Jules Sparoni where he no longer will be able to do harm."

"Anyone else on the Star news staff would have done as well."

"You're too modest, Dan."

"No, I'm not. I'm merely stating a fact." Dan thrust both legs toward the floor and slid out of his bed. Billy's words made him anxious to report for another assignment, to get back into harness. Newspaper work was in his blood and as much a part of him as his unruly dark hair and friendly grin.

"Say, Billy . . . When do we eat?"

"You mean . . . When do *you* eat. I had my dinner at the Riverside Tea Room over an hour ago. Leave everything to little Billy. I'll fix something for you. I'm off to the ice chest. If there's nothing in it, I'll fix you some lovely cornflakes or some wheatena."

Billy started toward the door. Dan leaped with sudden alacrity toward him, seizing one of the pillows from his bed. He hurled it at the retreating back. "See that you find something more than cornflakes," he ordered.

"Phooey!" snorted Billy Parker inelegantly.

Dan finished dressing and sauntered into the

kitchenette, where Billy was bending over the stove. He was ravenously hungry. The hours of sleep had given him a fine appetite.

Dan held in his hand the special delivery letter he had overlooked that morning. He had opened it and had read the contents. A happy grin lighted his face. When he spoke his voice was clipped, excited.

"Billy . . . Did you see this letter?"

"Of course. I put it on the table beside your bed. From your expression, it must be good news."

"It *is* good news—the best ever! I just found and opened it a moment ago. I didn't see it when I crawled into bed. I was too tired, I suppose."

"Get to the point. Who is it from—and what is it about?"

"It's from my uncle Ray Hyland's lawyer in Norfolk, Indiana. Ray Hyland published the Norfolk Clarion, a weekly newspaper, for twenty years. He built the Clarion up, Billy, from almost nothing into the most powerful weekly newspaper in the state of Indiana. His lawyer in Norfolk, Vincent Markey, has written to me."

"Why . . . Why? Explain—before I burn your eggs," Billy ordered threateningly. "Didn't you tell me that your uncle Ray had sold the Clarion—had moved to Hollywood to write screen plays and dialogue for the movies? He's supposed to be working for Stupendous Pictures Corporation. Only last month we saw Randy Howell, the western star, in one of Ray Hyland's stories."

"That's right. He did sell the Clarion and he is in Hollywood, but Vincent Markey in Norfolk will always be his lawyer."

"Then . . . What's all this about? When lawyers write letters, they're usually rather important."

"This one is no exception. It *is* important."

Billy was disgusted. "Give me the facts, or let me read them for myself," he demanded.

"I'm giving them to you. According to Vincent Markey, the legal man, I've just been handed a nice piece of property. A lovely little gift has come my way."

Dan glanced again at the letter, as if to reassure himself.

"Billy, I've just been presented with my uncle's old weekly newspaper! I'm now the proud owner and publisher of the Norfolk Clarion!"

"You're fooling!"

"No, I'm serious—in earnest."

"I thought your uncle sold his paper to someone from New Jersey—some person outside the family. You once said yourself that he got rid of the Clarion before shoving off for California and the sunshine and open air grocery stores."

"He did sell the Clarion."

"Then how can he give it to you?"

"Let me explain. Ray Hyland sold the paper to some fellow from Haddonfield, New Jersey. But the new owner hasn't been successful in Norfolk—can't operate the Clarion on a paying basis. The new owner has defaulted—has fallen hopelessly behind in his payments, so the old sheet has reverted back to my uncle."

"I'm beginning to understand now."

"Fine." Dan grinned at him.

"I suppose he doesn't want to run the paper now that he's in Hollywood and making a name for himself, as well as plenty of money, as a writer."

"Exactly. Exactly."

"He wants you to run his old love, the Clarion—and he practically gives it to you."

"Again you're right."

"Fine, Dan. Now it's up to you to supply the details."

"There's not much more to say, I suppose. He *has* made me a present of the paper. That's the main thing."

"Are any strings attached to the gift?" Billy Parker inquired wisely.

"I don't think so."

"None at all?"

"I haven't been able to find any. I will give up my job here and move to Norfolk. I will appear in Markey's office and sign a document. Then the Clarion is all mine. That's all there is to it. Here, read the letter for yourself." Dan handed it to him and looked longingly at the meal Billy had prepared.

"Can I eat now?" he asked.

"Sure. Pitch in while I read."

Dan Hyland did not need further invitation. He immediately began to make the food before him disappear.

Billy talked as he read. His friend somehow managed to answer him, but often replies were muffled by large quantities of scrambled eggs. "I suppose your uncle can't resell the Clarion, so he has decided to unload it on you. I hope he's not handing you a sour lemon."

"I don't think I've got a dud on my hands. Uncle Ray built the Clarion into a real newspaper—into the top notch weekly newspaper in the state and undoubtedly the most profitable."

"How long has he been in Hollywood, Dan?"

"Five years, I think."

"I thought so!"

"What's the matter? Why are you crowing?"

"Simply this: your uncle reaped his profits during prosperous years—during the good old days when almost everyone made money—plenty of it, too. Ray Hyland sold his paper in a year of prosperity—a year of tremendously inflated values. It is reasonable to suppose that he asked and received more for the Clarion than it is actually worth today."

"Just what are you trying to put across, Mr. Wise Man?"

"Something very simple—something astonishingly easy for even a lame brain like yourself to comprehend."

"Go on. I'll listen, even if you are insulting my intelligence and good name. Talk on, Billy."

"Ray Hyland sold the Clarion five long years ago. A lot has happened since then."

"You're telling me!"

"I'm telling you that five years ago your Clarion was a prosperous, respected weekly newspaper. What is it worth now?"

"Whew! You've got me there, pal. I don't know what it's like now. I really don't. I've kept thinking that it's practically the same great paper Uncle Ray sold to the unfortunate man from New Jersey."

"——And little Billy is beginning to make you do a bit of worrying. Isn't that it? You're

beginning to wonder what the paper is like now.
For all the information you have, it may be in
a near bankrupt, down-at-the-heels condition. It
stands to reason that this Jersey guy must have
had a struggle with the sheet, or else he'd have
been able to keep up his payments on it to your
uncle."

"Bright boy!"

"There's nothing especially bright in what
I've been explaining."

"Have you anything more to say?" inquired
Dan.

"No, I haven't."

Dan finished the last of the all too small meal
before him and shoved his plate away. He was
distinctly pleased with himself, and even Billy
Parker's teasing had failed to ruffle his char-
acteristic good humor.

"You know, Billy, I'm willing to wager everything I now have in this cruel world that my
uncle knows all about the more than likely run
down present condition of his old newspaper."

"Of course he does. He also is aware of the
fact that you're considered quite a newspaper
man around Chicago. He's throwing the Clarion
in your lap to discover what you'll make of the
sheet. He's testing you, Dan, and I want you to
chase down to Norfolk, take over the Clarion,

and make good—whatever the odds against you may be."

"Thanks for the kind words and pep talk."

"I know you, Dan, and I'm sure you can be a real success in Norfolk. You're just what the doctor ordered for the Clarion. You're a newspaper publisher now, and you're going to put your own paper at the top."

"Hurrah for the Norfolk Weekly Clarion!" Dan cheered.

"Hurrah for Dan Hyland, newspaper publisher!" added the confident Billy Parker.

"Say," hushed the new Clarion owner, "we'd better be a little more quiet. Somebody may object to our cheering."

"Let 'em object. It won't do 'em any good." Billy was still shouting enthusiastically. "You're no longer a reporter, my lad. You've graduated. 'Publisher and Editor' is the title now."

"But I'm still a newspaper man."

"Sure—always a newspaper man."

"Say, I can hardly believe I'm the owner of a real newspaper."

"You are. Don't forget that, fellow. Golden opportunity has knocked at your door. Now let's go downtown to the office and inform George Anderson Gargan of the sad loss he is about to experience. He is going to lose his star reporter!"

"I wish I could be as enthusiastic about all this as you are. I'll hate giving up my job on the Star."

"Why worry about the Star? Laddy, you've been presented with the chance most newspaper men pray for—and on a silver platter at that."

Billy pounded on the table top, rattling the dishes and causing them to jump and dance merrily, lending emphasis to his loud words. One of the dishes suddenly clattered to the floor, shattering into sharp, jagged pieces. Undeterred, Billy went on even more boisterously than before.

"On to Gargan's office," he cried. "On—into the lion's den. You're practically in Norfolk, Dan. Soon you'll be battling for the Clarion— fighting to put it back on its high pedestal— fighting for the success you'll deserve."

Dan smiled at the other's enthusiasm. Courage flamed in his eyes and there were lines of determination in his pleasant face. Dan faced the future unafraid.

CHAPTER IV

The Unexpected

GEORGE ANDERSON GARGAN regarded the first edition of the Daily Star with an intense scrutiny which was somehow quite detached and also at the same moment critical. After throwing the still damp newsprint into a waste basket, he gave his attention to the young man before him. He frowned.

Icy fingers trailed up and down the young man's spine.

Gargan next pretended to be busy reading a letter. When he again turned his gaze toward his visitor, there was a twist of something like grim humor about his mouth as he uttered a slight sound, unrecognizable either as a greeting or a warning. Then came harsh words.

"What do you want, Hyland?"

The managing editor spoke as if the whole world were conspiring against him, trying to rob him of precious time and energy.

"I came in on a matter of business."

Dan had not misplaced his voice altogether, and he was fast losing his fear of the other's hoarse commanding tones. Gargan's bark was much worse than his bite.

"What business?" There was mock despair in the tone. "Don't you know I'm busy?"

"Yes, I know that, but I've got something extremely important and personal to talk over with you. That's why I'd like to speak with you now—right away, if I may."

"Very well. Go ahead. I'm listening."

Gargan folded his hands over his large stomach and gave the young reporter his complete attention. Under his gruff exterior he was a kind man and glad to talk with the men under him on the Daily Star staff.

Dan did not waste words. With a malicious little inward smile he dropped his bombshell.

"I'm leaving the Star, Mr. Gargan." He said quietly, as if he were discussing the weather.

"What?" The single uttered word was questioning and incredulous.

"I want to give up my job. I'd like to leave the Star."

Suddenly the big man behind the mahogany desk began to laugh. He seemed to be enjoying a great private joke and the obvious bewilderment and wonder of Dan Hyland increased his mirth to a point where it was necessary for him to hold his sides and to grip the wood for support. Dan, not knowing what to make of the exhibition, remained perfectly still, his puzzled face clearly indicating his astonishment and surprise.

"So you want to leave the Star?" Gargan roared. "I've been expecting you to come bouncing in here with that sort of speech for two weeks."

"I don't understand, Mr. Gargan."

"You will in a moment."

Gargan, now trying hard to become once again the sober managing editor, pressed one of the many electrical buzzers arranged near the edge of his desk.

"I've been expecting you to resign from the staff for almost a month. In spite of my being prepared for such a scene, you startled me badly a moment ago. So I had to laugh at my own reaction to your pretty little speech of resignation."

"I'm still in a fog," Dan admitted truthfully. "I still can't understand how you knew I was thinking of giving up my job. Only very recent developments have made it necessary for me to leave."

"Be patient," the editor suggested, "and I'll explain." He fluttered what was intended as a soothing hand.

Ashley Church, the attractive secretary, entered the office, responding to the buzzer signal. She was efficient in a rather prim, detached way and lovely to gaze upon. Gargan liked her as a competent, brainy secretary; the young men of the Daily Star considered her an exciting and comely contrast to the dull newspaper office surroundings. Miss Church smiled archly at Dan Hyland and then turned inquiringly to her employer, who barked, "Get me the file containing my recent correspondence with Mr. Ray Hyland."

CHAPTER V

Challenge!

DAN HYLAND leaned forward and carefully replaced upon Gargan's desk the file of correspondence he had been given to read through. The four letters from his uncle, all received and answered within the previous three months, had been mailed from Hollywood and chiefly concerned Dan and the Norfolk Clarion.

The new newspaper owner raised smiling eyes to meet the equally amused ones of the managing editor. Dan had never before seen his chief in such a fine good humor. The crankiness which had greeted him on his entrance had quickly changed to a happy mood and spirit far more pleasant.

"These letters certainly speak for themselves," Dan declared. "You and my uncle seem to have been cooking up this Clarion ownership proposition for me for some time. I suppose my resignation from the Star reporting staff is now accepted."

"Not so fast, Dan." Gargan raised a cautioning

48

finger. "I want to have a serious talk with you before you leave the Star, and right now is as good a time as any, I suppose. Can you remain here for a little while and listen to what I have to say?"

"Surely. I can stay here all night," Dan laughed.

"That will hardly be necessary." Gargan smiled inwardly at the new publisher's enthusiasm. He was a little wistful, too. Once he had been young like the boy before him—young, optimistic, and filled with unbounded enthusiasm. And now an old friend had placed a great responsibility upon him. He fully appreciated the importance of the role which Ray Hyland in far away California had called on him to play. He framed words and sentences in his mind. Dan must start off on his new career on the right foot. He, George Anderson Gargan, would do his utmost to insure a proper beginning.

Dan settled back in his chair and prepared to listen. He respected Gargan, respected him as a man and as a great and clever editor.

The men who work for Gargan may fear him, may shy from contact with him because of his well known caustic tongue, but they also admire and respect him because of his brilliance. He symbolizes the strength and the power of modern journalism. His stern bearing means responsibility, and permanence. He is the Simon Legree of the Chicago Star, the whip-cracker and law-giver, but he is also security and refuge.

It was Dan Hyland's privilege to behold Gargan in one of his most human moments. For the next thirty minutes the editor of the Star became young and enthusiastic again and recovered for a precious half hour the ardent eagerness usually guarded by gigantic layers of dignity, both physical and mental, necessary to one of his position. The voice of power, usually carrying a strong note of weary insolence, became the eager voice of a man who relives the triumphs of his youth through helping another begin his career as an editor and publisher.

"I'm going to be very frank with you," Gargan declared candidly. "I don't want you to go down to Norfolk and get your inexperienced young head knocked off."

Dan's pulse quickened. Excitement might loom ahead! The other's warning and tone promised adventure.

"What do you mean, Mr. Gargan?"

"Exactly what I said. I want to warn you fully before you leave Chicago, so you won't get into trouble. Man to man, Dan, running the Norfolk Clarion is going to be more than difficult for you.

Your uncle and I, close friends ever since we started together on the old Chicago Inter-Ocean, think you stand a fair chance of coming out on top."

"And why is publishing the Clarion going to be the opposite of easy? You haven't explained that as yet."

"Give me time, youngster. I've been preparing you for the most important part of what I've got to say." The editor reached for an odorous old pipe and carefully filled it with tobacco from a pouch before him on the desk. Dan waited patiently until the pipe was finally lighted. Its owner indulged in a fragrant puff or two before continuing.

"When Ray Hyland went to California, he sold the Clarion to an eastern chap. I think the name was Miles—Toby Miles, and he had the reputation of being quite a small town newspaperman, but he failed utterly with your uncle's prize paper. Now it's but a ghost of its old self. When Ray left for Hollywood it had a circulation of over five thousand—complete coverage of the city. At the present time, I understand, the circulation is barely eight hundred and advertising is conspicuous in the sheet because of its absence. Putting it harshly, the Norfolk Weekly Clarion is almost a dead thing. In its present state of near collapse, there is practically no excuse for its existence."

"Is there a rival paper?" Dan asked mildly. Already the light of battle was in his clear eyes; already he was beginning to gird himself for a fight which would end in triumph or in ignominious failure. He was anxious and ready to do far more than his best. Like all masterful generals, his first thought was concerned with gaining a thorough mental picture of the "battleground."

Gargan nodded. "Yes, there is a rival weekly. It's the Post-Ledger, operated by the political party now in control of the city. Because of the strong backing, it is quite a powerful paper with a good deal of influence, but not overly disposed to champion the rights of Mr. Average Citizen. The Clarion used to do just that, even in the face of seemingly overwhelming opposition from the politicians, shysters, and others with selfish interests."

Quite breathless with interest, Dan again had a question.

"What happened when Toby Miles took over the Clarion?"

Gargan stared at his littered desk and meditatively sucked his briar, reflecting on an answer.

"Can the fall of the Clarion be blamed on hard times?" prompted his young listener.

"No—no, not entirely."

There was a pause, then George Anderson Gargan spoke again.

"The real reason for the decline of the Clarion lies elsewhere," continued Gargan. "Miles, shortly after he began to publish the paper, allied himself with the wrong crowd. He inadvertently grew friendly with the shady interests Ray Hyland had fought for years, and so the people of Norfolk turned against him and against the paper. Soon the politicians and selfish interests had him under their thumb, and then came the beginning of the end. The Clarion lost circulation and prestige. Advertisers overlooked the sheet when placing contracts."

"But how about the other newspaper, the Post-Ledger—the paper owned outright by the party in political control? Why did it grow? How could it prosper?"

"I'm coming to that. You've been around Chicago quite a bit on Star assignments. You know the ropes pretty well."

"Thanks for the compliment. I *think* I know my way about."

"All right, tell me something."

"I'll do my best," Dan promised, pleased.

"What is the most effective method used by politicians to throw suspicion away from them-

selves during times when their shadier operations are threatened with exposure?"

Dan had only to think for a second before he
had an answer ready. "That one's easy," he
laughed.

"Well, what's your answer?"

"The good old 'smoke screen' is the device
usually brought into action. Am I not right, Mr.
Gargan?"

"You are." The editor smiled.

"How does the famous 'smoke screen' apply
in Norfolk?"

"Norfolk has been run for many years by an
unscrupulous political 'boss' of the type often
met in fiction but seldom encountered in real
life. This man, Con Sheldon, has directed the
political destinies of Norfolk for two decades.
He also has rather shady underworld connections. Your uncle fought him with some success,
but the battle lapsed when he left.

"Con Sheldon directs attention away from his
own underworld work and crooked operations
by using the Post-Ledger to fight an imaginary
enemy. The Post-Ledger makes a big fuss over
nothing and throws dust in the eyes of the average
citizen. The sheet provides an effective smoke
screen for the main purpose of concealing the
rotten quality of the Sheldon city and county

administration. At the present time the Post-Ledger is making a big fuss over the alleged wicked machinations of the big city bankers and the railroad and power companies. The Chicago and Southern railroad is suffering most of all at present."

"Some picture you're painting!" Dan exclaimed.

"And it's a true one. There's something else too."

Dan laughed. "Is there? Really? Let me hear the worst."

"Here's the 'something else' I spoke of. The Chicago and Southern people have been having more than their share of misfortune and criticism lately. The fast mail between here and Louisville has been held up and robbed of its precious cargo three times within the last few months."

"But what connection do these robberies have with the Clarion?"

George Anderson Gargan smiled wisely.

"I won't reply to that question," he said. "I think it will answer itself after you have been in Norfolk for a few days. You see, your uncle and I think quite a lot of you. We've been corresponding back and forth for some time. He wanted to know if I thought you were capable of handling the Clarion as it deserves to be handled. He had me investigate present conditions in Norfolk. That's why I've been able to hand out information and warn you against Con Sheldon and his gang. The city of Norfolk is unknowingly in the clutches of grafters; the Norfolk Clarion is in trouble—at present a poor excuse for a weekly newspaper. You, Dan, can rid Norfolk of Con Sheldon and his crowd. You, Dan, can put the Clarion back at the top of the list of Indiana weeklies. Your uncle and I are challenging you to make good! We're issuing a challenge. Get that!"

"I accept your challenge." The words were resolute, determined.

"I've got to get back to my work now," George Anderson Gargan told him, and once more the grizzled managing editor was his old self—hard, unbending. The moment of gentleness was over.

Dan glanced at his watch. "It's the press hour for the first city final," he announced.

"Yes, you're right. There's no more time for us to talk now. I know that, but I want to see you again just before you leave. Can you come in and see me sometime very soon?"

"I'll do that, Mr. Gargan. And thanks for all you've done for me."

Gargan snorted. "Youngster, you've done

something for me. You've made it possible for me to live over again some of the good old days. I wish I were going there with you—down to Norfolk to fight—back to your uncle's town to give Con Sheldon the licking he so richly deserves. You've got to make good, Dan!"

"I will," Dan declared. "I will." The words were spoken with quiet simplicity but his voice carried convincing power.

Suddenly thunder came from below, a churning and grinding of great monsters, and presently there floated up to the pair in the office the wail of night hawk newsboys. This was their world—the world of headlines and last minute deadlines and bitter circulation wars.

The presses roared. To Dan Hyland they shouted a battle song.

CHAPTER VI

Robbery in the Night

THE Chicago and Southern railroad's Midnight Special thundered through brooding blackness. The opened firebox of the locomotive painted the flying night a flaring, flaming red, and swiftly turning wheels clacked with rhythmical precision over matched rail ends.

The clatter and noise of the onrushing train was a cheerful song temporarily breaking a mournful silence. Crossing bells clanged momentarily, then their bright clangor tinkled faintly into oblivion as the big engine's whistle shrieked again, this time before roaring through a tiny village huddled close to the life-giving railroad.

The Chicago and Southern was quite a railroad. Its main track extended from Chicago to Louisville, a distance of three hundred and twenty-five miles. Many of the great rail systems had attempted at one time or another to acquire control of the road, but the Chicago and Southern's hard-boiled and old-fashioned president,

Vance Murray, had managed to stop all such efforts.

Vance Murray's railroad held a lucrative mail contract and each night found four or five heavily laden mail cars attached to the crack Midnight Special. The finest of engines pulled the Special, making the run to Louisville in less than seven hours. Leaving Chicago's Dearborn street station on the stroke of midnight, Number Four, the Special, could be counted upon to roll across the broad, swirling expanse of the Ohio river and into Louisville shortly after six thirty each morning of the year. In spite of the consistently eccentric schedules of most of the other trains on the C and S tracks, the Special was generally on time. There were no connections to be made— no flag stops and few regular ones.

Unfortunately for the peace of mind of Vance Murray and the safety of the United States mail carried on the night limited, daring bandits began to take an embarrassing interest in the train. Men, with no thought or consideration for the patrons of the mail service or the feelings of the railroad and the Post Office Department, robbed the Midnight Special of the precious cargo carried in its mail cars. Daring robberies, planned and executed with brilliant finesse, took place not once or twice, but three times. Baffled railway mail clerks first faced the business end of bandit guns near Dyer, Indiana, a way station only thirty miles from the Chicago terminal. The second hold-up took place further down the line between Pleasant Ridge and McCoysburg on a lonely stretch of track. The third raid was daringly carried out in the glare of the lights surrounding the LaFayette station.

The robberies were similar only in the uncanny cleverness of the men taking part in them. At Dyer gunmen jumped aboard the engine and mail cars as the train slowed down for the crossover on the edge of the little city. One of the gang then slipped back over the tender and mail cars and when an accomplice in the cab shoved an automatic into the back of the engineer, forcing him to bring his heavy train to a halt, the front Pullman of the train was neatly separated from the locomotive and mail cars. Then they looted at leisure as the mail cars and engine went on as far as the next station, leaving the Pullmans stranded a thousand feet south of the Dyer station. Having speedily accomplished their dangerous work, the mail bandits abandoned their "special" at St. Johns, disappearing into the protective black emptiness of the night.

A red flare, of the kind used by freight train

brakemen, brought the Midnight Special to a sudden, jerking halt two miles south of the deserted Pleasant Ridge station two weeks later. Bleak prairie stretched away from the train.

Grim faced men swarmed out of nowhere, surrounded the entire train, pointed machine guns at trainmen and mail clerks. And then, with their precious loot reposing beside the right of way, they motioned the train on toward McCoysburg.

The third and most recent of the painstakingly organized hold-ups occurred in the LaFayette station under the very station lights. It, too, was deftly planned, well executed by a gang of master bandits, men who would have made the famous Jesse James of almost legendary fame seem a mere pick-pocket in comparison.

Railroad police and government detectives were called into action, but could not learn the real identity of the "ghost gang" or capture a single member of the organization. All of the lootings had been carried out with expert precision. Each robbery had been staged so as to take advantage of the weaknesses in the defense of the guards in the mail cars—engineered deftly, with a sureness which was ruthless.

Vance Murray and the Post Office Department

faced the facts with alert eyes. They quickly realized the weakness of their position and set out
to do away completely with that weakness. First
of all they put armed guards on all Chicago and
Southern cars carrying registered mail—armed
guards who were quick on the trigger, guards
with machine guns even uglier than those owned
and brandished by the members of the "ghost
gang." The robberies stopped at once. But Vance
Murray was not to be fooled. He knew that extra
guards could not be kept in the registered mail
cars forever. He knew that the master criminals
who had plundered three times would strike
again, as soon as the guards' vigilance was relaxed. He realized that passengers were refusing
to ride on his railroad because of the danger in-
volved. His pride in his night limited train and
his pride in his railroad had been dealt a stunning
blow by the lawless men who had robbed and
would kill if anyone stood between them and the
sacks of treasure nightly aboard the Midnight
Special. Those men were probably biding
their time, slyly waiting and crouched ready to
spring.

So Vance Murray began to fight back. He
hired detectives and he sent to Columbia Uni-
versity for Lucian Kyle, the inventor of the
justly famous "Invisible Eye" and one of the

few men in the world who might really be able
to help him with his problem.

The Midnight Special roared onward, a rushing monster. Tower LR loomed out of the secretive darkness—a nest of friendly gleaming
light above the twin silver rails. Engineer Bob
Crowder opened wide the throttle controlling
his steam giant. Back in the registered mail car
grim men peered out into the night with machine
guns and high powered rifles ready beside them.

The whistle shrieked and cold, barren walls of
rock threw back its hysterical scream.

CHAPTER VII

The Ghost Gang

DAN HYLAND industriously pulled out drawers and dumped their contents into two huge suitcases and a small steamer trunk. He was almost ready to leave for Norfolk. Pausing from his labor for a moment, he surveyed his bedroom with a searching gaze which finally located a pile of shirts and ties heaped upon the bed. Dan sighed. Man-like, he reflected that they must be jammed in somewhere. The suitcases were already bulging, crammed with wearing apparel.

Billy Parker appeared in the doorway to watch his friend bring order out of chaos. Billy had no packing worries. He was remaining in the apartment and another Daily Star reporter, Jack Edwards, would move into Dan's bedroom in a few days. Billy had the appearance of permanence. Apartment mates might come and go but he would remain on at sixty-nine Longcommon Road.

"Need help?" Billy queried, his eyes roving over the piles of clothing, the yawning trunk, and the well filled suitcases. "Want another bag, Dan?"

"No thanks. I'll manage with what I have."

Dan went back to the task of inspecting pairs of sox. Those which had acquired holes larger than a one cent piece he promptly threw in the general direction of an already overflowing waste basket; other less damaged pairs were cast toward the larger of his two suitcases. It was necessary for him to discard over half of his supply.

Billy threw himself across the bed, occupying a narrow space between piles of clothing. "Are you taking the Chicago and Southern railroad's Midnight Special?" he inquired.

Dan looked up from his packing. "I am."

Billy looked cautiously about him, then spoke in an exaggerated stage whisper. ". . . Then beware! Beware!"

Dan grinned, amused by his friend's antics. "But why?"

". . . Because the Midnight Special has been robbed on three different and highly profitable nights."

"I'm safe, Billy. No bandit in his right mind would ever bother about me. All reporters are poor—and I'm one of the poorest. Look at the holes in this sock! I can't even buy new clothes, because I'm going to spend all my savings on the Clarion. I'll need every penny I've saved."

"You're not taking your money with you in cash, are you?" Billy questioned anxiously.

"Of course not. I'm taking no chances. My bank will send it to me—after I'm safely settled."

"When does your train arrive in Norfolk?"

"At five thirty tomorrow morning," answered Dan.

Billy Parker frowned. "I don't know why," he said in a puzzled voice, "but I'm afraid for you. There may be another robbery. The bandits might wreck the train."

"I'll be safer on that train than in Chicago," Dan assured him. "Some of Jules Sparoni's friends don't feel any too kindly toward me."

"You're probably right," Billy agreed.

"Of course I am. I'll arrive in Norfolk safely and take over the Clarion promptly at nine."

"Is Toby Miles still in Norfolk, Dan?"

"No. Miles left town a month ago. A chap named Leslie Wysong has been carrying on since he left, editing what's left of the Clarion. I expect to keep Wysong on as a sort of assistant editor—if he proves to be competent."

"Know anything about him, Dan?"

"Gargan and my uncle have each mentioned his name. I suppose he's some small town kid who thinks he knows all about journalism. I'll soon find out."

"I hope he's all right, Dan. You'll need an assistant at first, someone who knows the lay of the land, someone who has lived in Norfolk for a long time."

"You're correct there," the new editor-publisher continued virtuously. "I'll keep Leslie Wysong on in that sort of capacity. He's doubt-less young and inexperienced, and inclined to think he knows it all. I'll soon take the cock-sureness out of him and make him into a real newspaper man."

"Don't draw your conclusions until you meet Wysong," Billy warned. "He may be different from your idea of him."

Dan went back to the subject of the train robbers, all the while busily packing. "I under-stand the C. and S. railroad is going to do some-thing about those mail bandits," he said. "The president of the road, old Vance Murray, has called Lucian Kyle from New York."

"I don't follow you."

"It's all very simple. Kyle has invented a del-icate little photographic machine which Murray thinks will teach the naughty boys who have been looting his mail train a great lesson. The Chicago and Southern main line passes through Norfolk, and the Midnight Special stops there. C. and S. money is spent in Norfolk; many railroad workers make their home in the city, so naturally a large part of the population is interested in Vance Murray's railroad—interested in seeing the bandits caught."

"And where do you come in?" asked Billy in a bewildered tone.

"I enter the picture as the editor of the Norfolk Clarion. The Norfolk Clarion will assist Vance Murray in capturing the men who have robbed his pet train; the Clarion will take the lead in bringing the criminals to justice—even if its editor-publisher must turn detective and track them down himself.

"It'll be the Clarion's first big stunt—the first big service under my leadership. I'll show the rival sheet a thing or two and put my own paper back on the map with a vengeance. From now on the Clarion is with Vance Murray and after the ghost gang that robbed his Midnight Special."

Dan finished with his packing a half hour later and managed to close his trunk and strap the suitcases. Billy had borrowed a Daily Star press car and had parked it in the circular drive before the apartment house. With the aid of a janitor the baggage was moved out of the building and packed into the machine. Then Dan and Billy went back into the apartment to make a last inspection, and suddenly the new editor and publisher of the Norfolk experienced an unhappy moment of sadness as the parting moment neared. He was leaving the place which had meant home to him for many months. It was only natural for him to linger during his last trip about the apartment. He realized, suddenly, that he was losing more than a home. There would be no more early morning snacks in the bright little kitchen; there could be no more impromptu sham battles in the living room.

A feeling of intense loneliness swept through his being as he looked around the rooms which had meant comfort and friends and home. He was leaving. He might return, but only as an outsider. He resolutely fought down the unsettling emotion which gripped him and composedly faced the future.

"Ready to pull out?" Billy was at his side.

"I think so. I don't seem to have forgotten anything."

"All right. Let's go."

"How are we fixed for time, Billy?"

"There's none to spare," he was informed, "but there's a moment for everything you've planned.

We'll drive down to the office and then over to the station, just before train time."

Dan gave the apartment one long last look and then closed the door behind him. It shut with a final noisy click, and a chapter in his life was almost closed.

They went out the front door, leaving the apartment building behind, and a moment later were in the car. Billy slipped under the wheel and started the motor, and Dan climbed in beside him. They had carefully piled the baggage in the rear.

Billy deftly shifted into "first," swung around the drive, and headed for the nearest through street, Burlington Road.

George Anderson Gargan received Dan in his private office a half hour later. While Billy waited outside the Star building in the car, Dan had his last talk with the great managing editor. He stood near the door as his late boss did most of the talking.

"You're tackling a real job, Dan. It's a worthwhile one, remember that, but it's also a tough proposition."

"I realize that, sir."

"You have learned a great deal here on the Star. I've watched your progress and reported it to your uncle with pride. Now you're going to be forced to use all the resourcefulness at your command. You're sure to come up against some mighty tough problems, but you are going to through adversity. Experience will enlarge your horizon."

"Yes, sir."

"There are lots of big city newspapermen as clever and as talented as yourself, men right here on the Star, who would give their right arm for the chance you've been handed. Make good, youngster. There's a great future ahead of you— a real future. If you put the Clarion back on its feet, the sky will be the limit."

Gargan frowned down at his desk. "There— I've had my say. I've got to get back to work. That fool night city editor out in the "slot" has bungled another big story. Didn't go after sufficient coverage," he added in explanation.

Dan nodded sympathetically. His sympathies went out to the city editor, too. Gargan was almost impossible to please. He, Dan Hyland, had been fortunate in discovering the human side of the Daily Star's famous "Simon Legree."

"Thanks, Mr. Gargan. Thanks for your interest—and your advice. I'll do my best."

"You'll do more than your best, Dan. I'm sure of that."

It was a great compliment, sincere, almost a tribute—a fitting end for an important day in the life of Dan Hyland.

The train with its long line of sleek steel cars waited in the Dearborn station. A steel engine coughed restlessly at the far end of the platform, its heart a red inferno of flame. Two gnome-like men, equipped with goose-necked oil cans prowled about the stirring mass of metal, preparing for swift flight. Live, hissing steam would move it the three hundred and twenty-five miles to Louisville, Kentucky.

"Here we are," Billy said, setting down the bag he was carrying before the steps of a Pullman. "This is your car, Dan."

Dan glanced at his tickets. "You're right."

The porter took care of the baggage, boosting it to the vestibule. The two young men, whose paths were to separate so soon, talked of trifles, masking their true feelings with light words, but each was fully aware of the other's deep friendship.

On the stroke of midnight there was a loud clanging of bells and uniformed trainmen swung lanterns and shouted the famous words which are as old as railroading itself.

"All aboard! All aboard!"

Dan clasped Billy Parker's strong young hand in a grip of iron. They put true feeling into their last handshake, smiled at each other with a fine understanding.

"Take care of yourself, Billy."

"I will, Dan, and I'll come down to Norfolk as soon as I possibly can. I might be able to make it in a few weeks."

"I'll see you then. S'long, Billy.

"So long, Dan. Give Norfolk a taste of the good old Daily Star fighting spirit. Win your battle!"

"You bet," said Dan softly, simply. He swung aboard the train as it jerked forward and began to roll out of the station. His friend after a last hearty smile turned his back and strode swiftly away, down the platform toward the station building.

The Midnight Special, train of trains, was on its way, roaring down dark, silent canyons of freight cars. Its swiftly turning wheels sang a new song to the young man in Lower Ten in the third Pullman—a song of exhilaration, a mighty symphony of power. As Chicago, a city with an appealing personality all its own, rushed by in the concealing darkness, Dan Hyland faced the future with a gay smile and a light heart. He was on his own now and the new chapter which was opening before him gave every indication of proving thrilling. And the Midnight Special might have an important place in that chapter too.

There were no welcoming crowds at the Norfolk station at five-thirty the next morning when Dan stepped from the Pullman vestibule into the dark Indiana early morning. Few Norfolkians were about. Ahead there were only the station agent and an assistant. A lone passenger alighted from the coaches. A shabby little man, the town hackman, stood before the station, vigorously rubbing his hands together. A battered taxicab, almost as nondescript as its driver, was parked at the far end of the brick platform.

Dan tipped the darky Pullman porter and walked away from the train. His baggage had been unloaded onto the platform. The hackman came toward him.

"Want a taxi, mister?"

"Yes, I do."

"Where to, mister?"

"The hotel, I suppose."

"That'll be the Norfolk House, sir, if you want the best hotel."

"Very well. Take me to the Norfolk House."

The taximan nodded and went after Dan's

baggage. The new owner of the Clarion walked toward the taxi, the heels of his brown suede shoes clicking cheerfully on the platform bricks. Despite the early hour and the lingering darkness, his smile was sunny. He was beginning anew! That in itself was tremendously thrilling. The feeling of wonderful exultation which had possessed him the night before was still a lively part of him. This was his first morning in Norfolk—his first morning as editor-publisher of the Clarion. He'd show Con Sheldon and the Post-Ledger a thing or two!

The Midnight Special had paused but briefly in Norfolk. The sacks of local mail had been quickly unloaded into the post office mail truck. The train was already slipping past Dan as he reached his taxi. Soon the train was little more than a smudgy streak of black smoke against the horizon, now tinted with the first rosy coloring of the rising sun. Later on the day might become uncomfortably warm, but now there was a fresh, damp coolness in the air which was distinctly stimulating. Dan Hyland filled his lungs with that morning air. He arrived in Norfolk, Indiana, as Cæsar moved into Gaul—ready to conquer, brave, prepared.

When he stepped in front of the cab, he had an unobstructed view of his new home city—his

battleground. Main Street started at the Chicago
and Southern station and ran East and West.
The business establishments of the little city occupied the two-, three-, and four-story buildings lining the main stem. A single street car
track was set in the middle of the pavement,
turning to the right when it came to the end of
the street. Dan also viewed the imposing county
courthouse on Front Street and the green of the
tiny courthouse park surrounding the big stone
building. Across from the station Morgan's department store announced an important sale with
gay streamers and fluttering pennants. Dan made
a mental note to call on the manager of the store
at his first opportunity. The city's largest retail
establishment, it should become one of the
Clarion's most important advertisers. Morgan's,
five stories tall, towered like a mountain above
the small stores and two story edifices on Front
Street. The Mutual Life building was the largest structure on Main Street. It occupied the
southwest corner of Main and Center. The City
Café, directly across from the station on Front,
threw out a typical early morning aroma of
steaming coffee and frying bacon. Streetlights
along Main Street were still lit and gleaming
palely.

   Dan's driver was back with the bags, which he

piled in the front of his machine. Dan introduced himself as he climbed into the cab. "I'm Dan Hyland," he said. "I'm the new editor and owner of the Clarion."

"Glad to meet you, young man. Are you Ray Hyland's nephew? Ray wrote Charley Sanders, who runs the hotel, that you were coming. My name is Alf Goodhue."

"Yes, I'm Ray Hyland's nephew—and I'm glad to meet you, Goodhue."

They shook hands.

Alf Goodhue started his machine and they clattered down Main Street, swinging into Indiana Avenue three blocks further on. Another block brought them to the Norfolk House, a rambling four-story building of red brick with an old fashioned mansard roof.

Dan followed the taximan inside. The Norfolk House had a spacious lobby and the finest public dining room in the city.

Dan registered and was introduced to Charley Sanders, the owner. He arranged for a weekly rate and was assigned to a room and bath on the second floor. Sanders and the hotel's only bell boy escorted him upstairs and made him comfortable in room 28. Three wide windows opened onto Indiana Avenue. Dan looked out upon the waking town and then began to unpack his bag.

How would Norfolk receive him? Would he like Leslie Wysong well enough to keep him on as an assistant? When would he meet Con Sheldon?

Seven men sat silently waiting in a shabby room over Norfolk's second hand furniture store, and their well cut, stylish clothes were a marked contrast to the poorness of their surroundings. They all were gathered around a much scarred round table. The air was blue with tobacco smoke, the fumes accenting the stuffy closeness of the place. Light came from a single glaring bulb in an unshaded wall socket—cruel brightness which brought out in bold relief the hard lines of the set faces. The one window was closed, the blind drawn.

"Watson'll be here any minute now. I heard the Midnight Special whistle for the station," said the leader of the seven.

The silence had been broken by a big heavy man with a florid, flabby face and an unruly crop of iron gray hair. Con Sheldon was fifty years old. He had a loose mouth and creases of cruelty running down from little bulging eyes. Avarice, cunning, and ruthless power were indicated in that remarkable face with its too-knowing smile. He was obviously the leader and the law giver.

The others about the old table listened respectfully, nodding in agreement.

Dave Dempster, Sheldon's trusted associate, was playing cards with Bo Martino and Joe Riley, two of the strong arm squad.

"I hope Watson got the Kyle plans," Dempster remarked. He was lean and sleek and his sharp eyes were quick and roving; his black hair was touched with gray about the temples.

"They *are* extra important," Con admitted. "We can't rob Chicago and Southern registered mail cars again until we find out what kind of a device that New York inventor, Kyle, has rigged up to catch us. We can't rob again until we know exactly what we'll be up against when Vance Murray finally takes the army of guards off the trains and substitutes Lucian Kyle's invention. I understand it's some sort of photo-electric gadget which will make it plenty tough for us if we try another stick-up."

"I think we're crazy to keep on picking on the Chicago and Southern," Dave Dempster declared, lighting another cigarette. "There are other railroads carrying mail cars."

"Listen, you fool." Con Sheldon's voice was menacing, hard and cold. "You'll carry out my orders, see. I'm the boss. I'm the boy with the power. I'm the gent that hands down the orders,

and I make all the plans. If you didn't have me
to plan your robberies, you'd never get anywhere."

There was truth in his words. Con Sheldon
with his political connections and his scheming
mind was the brains of the famous ghost gang.
Con Sheldon received graft from county and
city officials; Con Sheldon also bossed the ghost
gang, directing activities and planning raids.

"Sure, Con," one of the gang placated, "you're
right. You're the boss, but why don't you let us
hold up the mail trains on another road? The
C and S boys are on the look-out for us now. We
almost failed on that La Fayette stick-up. If we
hadn't timed our raid perfectly, we'd have all
been caught or shot."

"——And who planned the perfect timing
that saved your necks? I did. Who was able,
through political connections, to keep the La
Fayette police away from the North Street station on the night you fellows pulled the job?
And who owns the newspaper which managed
to convince most of Norfolk that a Chicago gang
is to blame for all the trouble? *I* am the answer
to those questions."

"You're right, boss," Dave Dempster agreed
in a conciliatory tone.

"Of course I'm right. And the ghost gang will

continue to rob the Chicago and Southern mail train because we're right here on the spot. We know this section of the country like a book. We know what we're up against, so we can plan for emergencies. Each robbery can be planned and executed perfectly, as if it were on a stage—as if it had been rehearsed carefully in advance."

"I'm beginning to get you now, Con."

"We'll pull two more robberies," the leader went on, unmindful of the interruption, "and they'll both be staged near Norfolk on ground we all know well. Our safety lies in perfect planning and in knowing just where to board the Midnight Special."

There were nods of approval. Sheldon had put across his point with forceful cleverness. The man was a natural leader. In deft, curt words he had painted a picture in the minds of his hearers and had made them realize for themselves how helpless they would be without him. Conway "Con" Sheldon was proud of his power over politicians and the underworld. When he spoke again the lash was gone from his voice. This time it was calm, completely persuasive.

"Here's our plan for the next few weeks." He paused for a moment as the six others leaned forward, interest and expectation clearly written on their faces.

Con Sheldon went on. "We're going to lay low for several weeks, until the guards are taken off of the Midnight Special and Lucian Kyle's protective invention is installed in substitution."

"Then what, Con?" Dave Dempster crushed out his cigarette.

"Then we strike—hard—twice, and we're through. Each of us will have at least a hundred thousand dollars in loot. We'll leave the racket before our luck gives out. Two more big robberies and we're through. Understand?"

"Sure, Con." The words came in a chorus.

"After our last hold-up each of you will be free to do as he likes, but until that time you must do as I say—carry out my orders to the letter, whether you like them or not."

The six nodded. Con Sheldon calmly reached for a new cigar.

"How about Lucian Kyle's protective photo-electric invention—the gadget that is supposedly going to keep us off the mail trains?" Tom Mayo, one of the group, put the question to their leader.

"Watson is helping us," Sheldon informed him. "He stole duplicate plans of the invention in Chicago. By studying them we'll learn how to make it useless in an emergency—we'll be prepared to work around it in our last two robberies.

When Vance Murray installs the invention in his registered mail cars, we'll be all ready for him, and when he feels secure and takes the armed guards off of the trains—well, we'll strike—twice."

As Con Sheldon finished speaking a faint shuffling sound came from the hallway outside the door. A moment later they all heard an intricate knock.

"That's Watson." A relieved smile crossed Con's hard features. The piggish eyes were gloating. "He must have the Kyle invention plans. We're off to a fine start."

Corbin Watson, Sheldon's right hand undercover agent, entered the room, and a smile of jubilant victory spread over his homely face. He was agile, and an adept at petty larceny.

"I stole a duplicate set of the Kyle invention plans from the old boy's hotel room," Corbin Watson announced proudly. "It was easy, so here they are." He dumped a fat manuscript case on the table.

"Are you sure they're the actual plans?" This from Dempster.

"Well, we'll check for ourselves." Con Sheldon picked up the case. "You haven't muffed a job yet, fellow. This would hardly be a good time to start, eh?"

"You said it, boss." Corbin Watson grinned. He had great admiration for Sheldon. Little boys admire circus acrobats and street car motormen. Simple Corbin Watson was completely devoted to the powerful Sheldon. Praise from him was like wine to the lesser man. He enjoyed considering himself Sheldon's confidant. His feeling was dog-like, almost adoration.

"Ah, Corbin, you haven't failed me." Con Sheldon triumphantly held in his hands a complete set of the coveted plans.

Watson, anxious to keep the spotlight, went on to another subject he was sure would interest his hearers.

"Young Dan Hyland, Ray Hyland's nephew, arrived on the Midnight Special. I saw him get off the train, and Alf Goodhue took him to the hotel. He's in Norfolk to publish the Clarion."

Dave Dempster leaned forward anxiously. "Does his arrival mean anything, Con? His uncle once almost put you behind the bars."

An ugly expression crossed the flabby face. "Young Hyland won't bother us," Con Sheldon declared with slow emphasis. "I'm going to warn him—warn him to get out of town, and if he doesn't heed my warning——"

The final words remained unspoken. A look of hate finished the sentence.

CHAPTER VIII

Leslie Wysong Surprises

DAN emerged from the Norfolk House coffee shop and briskly set off down the avenue toward the Clarion publishing office on Dodge Street, three blocks distant. He wasn't worried and he was not afraid of the future. The steady sunshine of his own personal happiness would float him safely over the rocks in his path. All was right with the world and Dan Hyland.

The sun was hot overhead. The air had grown heavy; everything smelt piercingly sweet. The green of the trees had a bright sticky look, and the flowers in neat beds before the city hospital were small explosions of color. For Dan the tang of printers' ink was already in the air. His imagination was that vivid.

He viewed the Clarion building for the first time, two blocks further on. It was an unprepossessing single story structure of some length and badly in need of paint. Once white, the entire frame office and shop was now a dingy, unrelieved gray, grown ramshackle with the years.

Two dusty plate glass windows looked out on Dodge Street. Through an opened side window the new owner could hear the cheerful clatter of a job press. The entire block drowsed and dozed in the warmth of the sun. A nondescript dog trotted along beside Dan for a few yards and then deserted him to roll in the grass. Languid echoes of traffic crept in from busy Front Street, a block away.

Dan paused before the door leading to the office. Nothing was going to be gained by stalling. He might as well make the plunge, "break the ice" as the saying went. He drew a deep breath, opened the door, and stepped inside. And then the pent up breath left him in a long, contented sigh. This was all his!

His eyes eagerly swept the combination business office and editorial room. A big, old fashioned stove with an enormous pot-belly occupied the center of the room. The floor was of wood; walls and ceiling were smoky and faded. To his left, by the front windows, was an enormous flat topped desk, piled high with old newspapers, exchanges, and cut-outs from syndicate "mat" service books. There were three other desks, each groaning with papers, paste pots, copy paper, and typewriters. Long banners of galley proof sheets dangled from hooks set into the walls and into the sides of the old wooden desks. From the back of the building came the clicking sound of a busy linotype and the industrious song of the humming press first heard in the street. The air was saturated with the odor of newsprint and ink.

For the first time Dan Hyland noted that another person was in the room. A young woman, a rather pretty but competent looking young woman, was bending over a roll top desk, tapping away at a typewriter. She was extraordinarily attractive, Dan decided, even in the dim light of the dingy Clarion office. She possessed dark hair which curled daintily, and a fair complexion which no beauty parlor could possibly have originated. Dan Hyland was never blind to beauty, no matter where he encountered it. In his mind he complimented Leslie Wysong for his taste in selecting such an ornamental secretary. But where *was* the man? He should have been in the office, prepared for the arrival of his new boss.

The girl was obviously intent on her work. She had failed to notice his entrance. Dan coughed slightly, to attract her attention. Dark eyes were promptly raised to his—dark eyes which were smiling pools of good humor. She came toward him, moving with graceful ease.

"Can I help you?" she asked in a calm, smooth voice that somehow suited her.

"I'd like to see Mr. Wysong—Mr. Wysong, please."

"I—I don't understand." There were little quirks of curious amusement about the nice mouth. The trim figure advanced toward him another three feet. "There's no Mr. Wysong here."

"What!" Dan tried hard not to make his voice seem too incredulous. He managed with a struggle. "What?—no Wysong here? Why—he's supposed to be the editor of this paper? I——"

The sentence remained unfinished. The obviously feminine young person across the desk was speaking. This time there was unmistakable laughter in her voice.

"There must be some mistake. You see, I'm Leslie Wysong, the temporary editor. I've been running things here for several weeks.

"——And I'm Dan Hyland," he laughed. "No one told me that Leslie Wysong was a young woman. You handed me quite a start."

"I'm sorry." She smiled again and Dan instantly came to the conclusion that Leslie Wysong was the prettiest young woman he had met in a long, long time. It was hard for him to imagine her as the competent newspaperwoman she obviously was. Leslie Wysong was very young and amazingly unspoiled, he decided. He remembered with a little inward grin the conversation he and Billy Parker had had just the previous day—the conversation which had featured Leslie Wysong as subject. He now was a trifle ashamed of what he had said.

"There's nothing for you to be sorry about," Dan assured her. "I'm the one to be sorry. I made a horrible mistake. No one told me in Chicago or at the Norfolk House, where I'm staying, that Leslie Wysong was an attractive young lady."

"You're not disappointed?" Leslie was anxious.

"No—I should say not. Quite the contrary, I'm pleased," the new publisher hastened to say. "Everything is so new to me here, I'm afraid I seem a bit bewildered."

The girl's face was sympathetic. "I can understand how you feel. I came here a stranger myself, two years ago, to become Toby Miles' secretary and helper. When he had to leave and give up the paper, I stayed on to keep the sheet going until your arrival. I've been barely able to manage. Toby Miles didn't leave much behind except debts."

"You were swell to carry on," Dan said. "I can't thank you enough."

"Forget it." She held out a slim brown hand. "I'm afraid I haven't greeted you in the approved chamber of commerce, booster club manner. Welcome to our fair city, Mr. Hyland."

"Dan," he corrected. "Dan's the name."

"Well, it's nice of you to dispose of formalities so quickly. You may call me Leslie—or Les. Les is my nickname."

"That's great—Les," he laughed easily.

She laughed too—a rich, deep-throated laugh. Quite suddenly they were friends, laughing together.

"You know," she told him. "I, too, received quite a shock when you walked into this office and introduced yourself. I rather expected Dan Hyland to be an old man with a long beard and stooping shoulders. Needless to say, my shock was a pleasant one."

"I never thought about Leslie being a girl's name as well as a man's," Dan admitted.

They laughed again, then were suddenly silent.

"Come in and sit down," Leslie suggested. "We must have a talk. I'll explain the present state of affairs to you fully, and I'll introduce you to the staff, and we'll visit Mr. Markey, your uncle's lawyer. Then you take over the reins, and run the paper without my help."

The very idea appalled him. He said so in no uncertain way, and the temporary editor of the Norfolk Weekly Clarion was obviously pleased, even a little flattered by his words—and his new offer.

"I'm glad you want me to stay," she confided. "I was hoping I wouldn't be tossed away like an old glove. But you're being more than generous—making me your assistant. Aren't you afraid I mightn't do?"

Dan shook his head vigorously. "You'll do, and you're going to stay on as my assistant. And you'll keep right on being editor until I get my bearings in this town. I don't know a soul aside from the hotel man, a taxi driver, and yourself. A good newspaper editor must know lots of people."

She nodded. Her quick mind was already forming a plan of action. Leslie Wysong was clever as well as ornamental. She and Dan Hyland would make a great team. It would be easy for them to work together, to create a new, greater newspaper.

"I've got a plan for the day," she announced. "Want to hear it?"

"I certainly do."

"Today, Friday, is our publication day. One of the high school boys comes in and delivers the paper to the present pitifully small subscription list."

"Don't worry, Leslie, our subscription list is going to start moving up with next week's issue."

"Those words do my old heart good."

They laughed again, the joyous sound causing one of the printers to look in on them through the glass port in the composing room door.

"If today is Friday," Dan said, "I have a whole week in which to get acquainted and learn the ropes."

"Right, Editor Hyland. Now here's my plan of action for today. First of all we'll visit the composing room and you'll meet the men out there and look over our physical equipment. Then you and I will come back here and have a long talk. You'll ask questions, and I'll do my best to answer them."

"Fine. And next?"

"Next we have lunch—at Ptomaine Joe's place."

"What a name for a restaurant!"

"We'll stop there for a bite because it's the lunch hour hang-out of most of Norfolk's business men—especially the younger crowd. I think you'll get along well with them. They're a great bunch, and I know they'll like you."

"——And after our luncheon?" he inquired.

"After lunch we call on your uncle's lawyer and then on the president of the chamber of commerce. If there's any time left, we'll come back here for more confab. Tonight you'll have to work alone. You can best spend the time going over our latest issue and the Clarion files, familiarizing yourself with the town and our advertisers. You might also glance at an edition of our rival newspaper. You'll get a well rounded idea of matters as they stand by doing all that."

"Say, you're a wonder," complimented Dan.

"Forget the praise, Mr. Editor. I'm not through yet. You're going to begin a busy week in less than three minutes. There will be meetings to attend, Rotary Club luncheons, and city officials to meet. I myself shall present you to Con Sheldon, the mighty boss of our fair city."

"I'm looking forward to that moment," Dan informed her. "I've heard of Sheldon."

"I'm looking forward to seeing him hung," Leslie Wysong spoke with grim humor.

"From all I've heard, that would be great," Dan agreed.

They were ready to visit the composing room. Dan Hyland had begun the first great battle of his life with competent Leslie Wysong as his able field marshal. Would the battle end in victory or crushing defeat?

CHAPTER IX

Sheldon's Bombshell

CON SHELDON'S strong gaze swept the little group of men. He knew those who faced him, knew them well. He knew their accomplishments and their minds and, more important, their failings. He stood in the center of the close room and allowed a full realization of his power over them to surge through his being. He was the leader, the big boss, and the law-maker.

The men in the meeting room waited expectantly. Something unusual was in the air. They all were sure of that.

The leader smiled inwardly. He had a most peculiar sense of humor, and he had just begun to perfect plans for a monstrous practical joke— a great practical joke to be played on the Chicago and Southern. Mail banditry was not enough for him. Something far more spectacular and difficult had entered his clever brain. He now planned to rob Vance Murray of his pride and joy—the famous Midnight Special! He had perfected a plan of devilish ingenuity—a plan which would

94

baffle government officials, famous detectives, and the entire world. He had worked it over in his mind until it was as completely perfect as any plan can be.

Sheldon cleared his throat loudly, then spoke.

"I've called all of you here again for a very good reason," he began forcefully. "I realize that we met in this same room but five hours ago, but since that time I have thought of something new, as important as it is startling. I want to tell you about that new 'something.'"

Dave Dempster was curious. "What've you got on your mind, Con? You've been grinning to yourself ever since I met you at the hotel. What's up?"

Sheldon went on. "When we left this room before breakfast, I took the Kyle invention plans with me. I wanted to study them."

"——And you did," added Dave.

"I studied them carefully." The speaker paid scant attention to the interruption. He was speaking slowly, choosing his words with great care and watching their effect on the faces of his cronies. "I studied them so carefully that they showed me the way to stage an absolutely safe robbery and at the same time pull the most colossal practical joke ever attempted."

He paused, watching his gang with sly cunning. Con Sheldon had never been inside a college, yet he was a master of crowd appeal. He had learned practical psychology in the streets, in secret meetings behind closed, barred doors, from the very mobs that had made him a political king and an underworld giant.

"Go on, Con," they chorused, all hungry for an explanation.

"I'm not ready to take you into my confidence yet. First, I want a pledge from each one of you. I want you to promise me that if I let you in on this huge practical joke of mine, you'll keep every detail of it a complete secret until I'm ready to make Vance Murray and the Chicago and Southern railroad the foolish laughing stock of the entire nation—of all the world, for that matter."

They promised, almost falling over themselves in their haste to assure him of their devotion, of their willingness to follow him blindly, without question.

"Now, one more thing," Con continued when the babble of promising voices had subsided. "I want all of you to understand what Lucian Kyle's invention will mean to us."

"We're listening, Con," Dave Dempster assured him.

"I want you to do more than listen."

Dave Dempster plainly showed the puzzled state of his mind. He was a clever crook. He could execute perfectly another's plans, after they had been carefully explained to him. "I don't quite get you, boss. What are you driving at?"

"I think you will understand in a moment. When I explain these plans which Watson took from Lucian Kyle's hotel room, I want you to think about them and study them for yourselves, just as I have gone over them for my own satisfaction."

"Why, boss?" This time Watson spoke.

"Because one man is seldom always right. I may have overlooked important points which you will notice. I want you to check me. I don't believe this invention of Kyle's is going to prove very dangerous to us, but I don't want to lull you into a false security. I don't want to overlook anything about this Kyle apparatus which may cause us trouble in a couple of weeks."

The others nodded wisely. "We get you, Con."

"I'll describe the invention to you," he went on. "It won't stop us because we will understand it and be ready for it when we rob the Midnight Special again, as its threat depends almost entirely upon the raiding party not knowing of its existence. The device which Lucian Kyle has perfected will be installed secretly in every registered mail car operated on the Midnight Special. Built into a different place in each car, it will be impossible to detect or put out of order without destroying the entire mail car!

"Lucian Kyle has perfected for the Chicago and Southern a very clever and delicate little motion picture camera and sound recording machine. It is very sensitive and tiny. Started almost automatically the instant a hold-up occurs, it will film clearly the entire robbery and at the same time make a sound record of the looting.

"This is what will happen. The camera and recording unit, neatly concealed, will begin to operate the moment we enter the registered mail car when our next robbery occurs. While we are sticking up the clerks and getting the mail, it will be busy photographing our faces and recording our voices. Then, after approximately three minutes have passed, the invention will automatically release a tear gas gun, which will fill the car with gas. First: the camera and microphone photograph and record the stick-up. Second: the tear gas gun cuts loose. That in a nutshell is Kyle's invention."

"Some machine!" Dave Dempster whistled.

"It will be impossible to find the hiding places

of the camera, microphones, recording machine, and gas gun. They will be built into the cars cleverly enough to escape detection. Fortunately for us, Vance Murray and the police have been working with the idea that the gang which has been robbing their mail cars will be caught unawares."

"What are we supposed to be afraid of?" Corbin Watson asked. "That invention of Kyle's isn't going to bother us. We'll wear masks to fool the cameras and get out of the cars before the tear gas goes off."

"Sure," Dave added. "We haven't got anything to worry about."

"Certainly we haven't," Con told him, "but that's not what I'm getting at. Vance Murray thinks Kyle's invention will keep us off the trains, or give us away if we do rob them, because he doesn't know that we're ready for him—all ready and waiting. He also believes that a known Chicago group of criminals is the famous 'ghost gang.' It wouldn't do him any good if he did get your pictures and a recording of your voices. See what I mean?"

They all nodded. Cruel lips widened in smiles.

"Now I want you to study the plans Watson stole for us, just to make sure there isn't something dangerous in them that I've missed. I don't think there is, but we're not going to take fool chances."

"Then what?" asked Corbin Watson.

"Then, in about two or three weeks, we'll play a huge practical joke on Vance Murray and the Chicago and Southern railroad—the big trick I told you about a few minutes ago."

Again they were hanging on his every word. Again he slyly watched their faces.

"I have inside information of a very interesting character," Con continued slowly, allowing his words properly to impress his hearers. "I was reliably informed this morning that Vance Murray has something else up his sleeve. He is building burglar proof compartments into the baggage cars carried on the Midnight Special, and in those burglar proof compartments Vance Murray plans to ship railroad pay roll money between Chicago and Louisville! Starting next month the Midnight Special will become a regular treasure train! It will carry a fortune in paper money once each week and also the registered mail!"

"But we can't rob those burglar proof compartments without wrecking the cars, and you can't do that in the short three minutes we'll have for pulling off the robbery," sighed Dave Dempster. "I guess we'll have to pass up the cash and stick to the registered mail." He sighed again.

"Don't be a fool." Con Sheldon's voice was like an electric bolt. It curled and lashed. "As I said before, we're going to play a big joke on Murray and his railroad and at the same time successfully stage two of the biggest robberies in history—hold-ups which will clean out mail and burglar proof baggage compartments, and the robberies will be carried out in absolute safety. No revealing motion pictures will be taken; no recordings will be made."

Con Sheldon smiled in triumph. He was ready for his mighty climax now.

"First, we rob—then comes my practical joke, the surprise which is going to create a mystery that will never be solved—a mystery which will make the Chicago and Southern people the laughing stock of America."

They waited for his final words. The silence was complete, intense. The big moment had arrived.

"We are going to make the Chicago and Southern railroad's Midnight Special disappear from the face of the earth! It will be robbed, its passengers will be forced to leave it, and then the engine and cars will roar on into the night—never to be seen again!"

Leslie Wysong pushed open the door leading to the Clarion's combination composing and pressroom, and the general office was filled with a sliding, thumping sound.

"Behold, the editor-publisher enters his new domain," laughed the girl. "Enter."

Dan strolled forward, following his feminine assistant closely and taking in the scene about him. The room was long, narrow, low-ceilinged and filled with the machinery typical and necessary to all small town and country weeklies. Two men were busily removing ink rollers from a small job press. Dan's hungry eyes missed nothing of the fascinating little world spread before him—the interesting miniature empire of linotype, papercutter, job press, paper folder, proof press, and big flat-bed, heavy duty Miehle press. A young boy, doubtless an apprentice printer, lugged discarded type from the steel form tables to the linotype's seething molten metal pot. The linotype was busily clicking away, its long, skinny mechanical arm lifting type slugs to their magazine. Still another printer was running the big Miehle. The pressman stopped his charge as he saw Leslie and Dan enter the room. Tipping his cap, he came over to where they were surveying the busy publication day activity going on all about them.

"Good mornin', Miss Leslie. Is there somethin' I can be doin' for ye?" The pressman touched his cap. His deep voice carried the thick brogue of old Ireland.

"No, Mike, there isn't anything. Everything seems to be going well this morning."

"Foin, Miss Leslie."

"But I'm glad you stopped the big press and came over, Mike. You see, I want you to meet your new boss, Mr. Hyland." She turned to the younger man. "Dan, this is Mike Ryan, the composing room foreman and pressman."

Dan smiled and shook the gnarled, ink stained hand offered by the printer. Mike grinned too.

"I'm glad to meet you, Mike," Dan said, "and I'm pleased to see things running so smoothly on such a busy day."

Complimented, Mike Ryan beamed. "Sure, things are goin' foin and ye have a mighty fine uncle, Mr. Hyland. I worked for him here many a year, and I'm glad to be workin' for his nephew."

"I'm afraid we're holding things up," Dan remarked, "and I don't want to do that."

Mike Ryan agreed. "I had better be gettin' back to me press."

"Well, when you have finished with this week's paper and have it folded and out on the street and on the way to our present pitiful subscription list, gather your men together and come into the front office. I'm taking charge of the Clarion today and, with Miss Wysong's help, hope to really make something important out of it. I'd like very much to talk to you personally and also with the men under you here in the composing room, so all of you come in and see me."

"That's a good idea, sir. I'll tell the men."

"When will you be finished with this week's issue, Mike?" The question came from Leslie Wysong.

"About two o'clock, Miss Leslie."

"Come in right after two, then. Mr. Hyland will have a little free time between two and three."

Mike Ryan touched his cap again and went back to the waiting, silent press. A moment later it resumed its task of printing copies of the Norfolk Weekly Clarion under his expert guidance. Leslie pointed out the others in the room, giving names and jobs.

"That's Monk Bradford at the linotype," she told him. "He's another one of your uncle's old staff—the only other one outside of Mike Ryan, I believe. The youngster carrying type is Biff Little, the printer's devil. He started with us two months ago and is learning fast. The man at the job press is Mike's assistant, Burt Marsh, and the fellow at the folder is a sort of general all-around helper. He is Vic Greer."

"I'll see all of the staff after two o'clock."

"We're ready to return to the editorial department," she informed him seriously. "And I'll do my best to give you a fair account of what has been happening to the Clarion since I've been on the staff, and we'll go over the books and business ledgers together, so you'll have some idea as to where you stand financially."

Leslie and Dan went into conference in the editorial office, and for the next two hours the young man from Chicago learned a great deal about country correspondents, local advertisers, "good will," country circulation, bad debts, Kiwanis and Rotary clubs, make-up, and reader interest. After the two hours with Leslie he had an excellent idea of the present state of Clarion affairs.

"So you see," Leslie finished, "you're in a fine position to go out and make something of this sheet. There aren't many big debts, and a real newspaperman like yourself ought to be able to go places and do things. You get what I mean, of course?"

He nodded and grinned. His grin was not forced. It was a natural grin, nice to see. He was beginning to feel very humble in the presence of Leslie Wysong.

"You flatter me," Dan brushed her compliment aside. "I'm just beginning to realize how little I really know about getting out a paper."

"You'll catch on fast," she assured him.

He was suddenly serious. "Do you think so?"

"Of course I do. In a few weeks you'll be running things as if you'd always lived in Norfolk. You must spend your mornings here in the Clarion office running the paper and writing local news; you must spend your afternoons and evenings out on the streets and at meetings, meeting people—getting the small town slant on life. That last point is very important. From now on, Dan, you must forget that you're a child of the city and become to all intents and purposes a small town lad."

"I'll do all you suggest," he agreed.

"It will be fun fighting Con Sheldon's Post-Ledger." She smiled in anticipation. "That weekly may not know it but it's in for a real battle."

Dan's voice carried intense enthusiasm. "We've just begun to fight! Now how about lunch?"

"I can't leave until Wes Reid arrives. He's a high school boy who writes up local news and helps me out with the proof-reading. He comes in every noon for an hour to relieve me. I'm sure you'll like him."

Dan relaxed against a handy desk and awaited the arrival of Wes Reid. Leslie Wysong disappeared into the composing room to give Mike Ryan instructions.

Mac Duncan, one of the Chicago Daily Star's rewrite men, reached for his telephone, plucking the receiver from its hook as the instrument jangled for the third time.

"Rewrite desk, Duncan speaking."

"This is Billy Parker and I want to report on that Kyle invention yarn. I'm at the Palmer House."

Duncan gripped the telephone receiver with one hand and reached for copy paper with the other.

Billy's voice droned facts over the wire. The Kyle invention plans were missing from the inventor's hotel room, and the police were blaming the theft on a handful of minor Chicago gangsters. Duncan's pencil made curious little shorthand marks on the copy paper. Billy had finished reciting facts and now was ready to start out for the Transportation building and a promised interview with Vance Murray. "Old Murray thinks a Chicago bunch of hoodlums robbed the trains those three times," he told Duncan. "Now I'm off to find out what he has to say about the theft of the plans. I'll ring you again later."

Dressed in a brown sport coat and pertly wearing a little hat which reminded Dan of a potato chip, Leslie Wysong again appeared in the Clarion editorial office.

"Wes Reid is in the composing room," she explained. "He came in the back way. You'll meet him later on. We can leave now." Her upturned face under the fashionable but outlandish hat was bright and eager.

"We're off then." Dan slid from his perch on the desk and joined her. "I'm afraid I'll disgrace myself. I'm that hungry."

"How, Dan?"

"Oh, I'll order soup and bend over the bowl to increase my efficiency—bend over too far. Then I'll fall in with a splash."

CHAPTER X

The Secret Room

CON SHELDON bent over a map of the state of Indiana, a dark scowl on his naturally none too pleasant face. Corbin Watson and Dave Dempster stood at his side, waiting for orders. Quite evidently, however, none were to be immediately forthcoming from the "big boss" of Norfolk. Sheldon was concentrating, his features screwed up with the effort. For him the men respectfully waiting by his side simply did not exist, so great was the problem with which he was wrestling.

After ten minutes of absolute silence had passed, Corbin Watson coughed loudly, bravely. The noise had the desired effect. Sheldon looked up, a little startled, from the map spread on the round table before him.

"What! Are you two still here? I had forgotten about you entirely. Are you waiting for something?"

"We're standing by for your orders," Dave Dempster reminded him. "You asked us to wait when the others left a half hour ago."

"So I did." The heavy face brightened. "I want you both to keep closely in touch with me for the next twenty-four hours. Corbin, you're not to go back to Chicago. For the time being I want you to keep an eye on young Hyland—the kid editor. I don't think he'll cause us any trouble, but I'm not going to take chances at this stage of the game. He might try to start something which would prove hard for us to finish for him, and a crusading newspaper editor is always a menace in a small town. I want you to report to me in this room at noon tomorrow."

"How about me, boss?" Dave Dempster was anxious.

"I've got plenty for you to do," Con informed him. "Get some sleep this afternoon, then come here at seven o'clock tonight. Bring Bo Martino and Riley with you. The four of us have a little business to take care of near Gosport. We're going to visit an old surveyor there—a fellow who once helped build part of the Chicago and Southern railroad."

Dave Dempster grinned understandingly at his boss.

"We're going to make a little friendly call, eh, Con?"

"Exactly."

"Guns, Con?" he queried.

"Of course."

"Anything else?"

"You might bring along a length of light rope, but the guns and masks are the most important things to remember."

"How about a car?" asked Dempster.

"We'll use a borrowed car, Dave. When you come with Riley and Bo Martino tonight, use a little discretion. Don't park in front of the building. I want our regular meeting place to remain a secret as long as possible."

"We'll all be careful, Con. We're not going to make a dumb break at this important stage of the game. You can depend on us."

"Fine. Remember this—I want both of you to meet me here at noon tomorrow."

"Noon tomorrow. It's a date, Con." The words almost came in a chorus. They were anxious to please him.

Sheldon's eyes wandered back to the map. "I'm perfecting my plans for the big 'practical joke' on Vance Murray and the Chicago and Southern," he told them. "Everything is working smoothly. Tomorrow afternoon the three of us will begin the actual preliminary work which will make it possible for us to carry out my big plans."

"Can we go now?" Corbin Watson asked, a

trifle anxiously. It was lunch time and he had had no breakfast.

"Sure, run along, but remember to keep an eye on young Hyland. He mustn't get in our way. After we take care of Vance Murray and his Midnight Special, we may have a little practical joke or two to pull on this Hyland kid. He shall suffer for all of the trouble his uncle caused me a few years ago. All right, Corbin, I have finished. You may leave, and Dave can go with you if he likes."

The two men left the secret meeting room and Con Sheldon went back to studying his map. The big shoulders hunched; the clever, evil mind plotted—concentrated on the ingenious plan he had been perfecting and completing since early morning. He grinned as he pictured the consternation his little "joke" would cause. He could imagine the black newspaper headlines now. The picture pleased him.

Smiling slightly, he drew a small circle in pencil around a black dot on the state map of Indiana. The "fun" would begin at that spot!

Dan Hyland sat across from Leslie Wysong at a small table and struggled mightily with one of Ptomaine Joe's steaks. His opponent was no meek, ordinary steak, but a tough, hardy specimen. Dan rested from his labors and summoned Ptomaine Joe's only waiter.

"How about a steel knife, buddy? I can't tackle this steak without one."

"Sorry—but we've only got one, and it's in use. You'll have to wait."

"Never mind," Dan told him with grim humor, "I won't bother with your nice tender steak. I'll stick to the side dishes."

"You'll know better next time," Leslie Wysong grinned at him over her plate lunch.

"I'll never battle with one of Ptomaine Joe's steaks again," Dan declared. "I have learned my lesson."

"I brought you here to meet the young business men of the town," Leslie went on, "and so far you have met only three."

"Nice fellows, too," Dan commented. "I was glad to meet them. I think I'm going to gain a small town slant on life within a very short time."

"I think so too, and four more merchants are just coming into the restaurant. We'll stop at their table on our way out."

"How about dessert?" asked Dan. "There are three kinds of pie from which to choose."

"——And all three of them are crossed off the menu," discovered Leslie. "No pie today, I guess."

"That's a mercy," Dan told her with a sigh of relief. "Somehow, I don't feel quite equal to the task of digesting one of Ptomaine Joe's pies. Let's have canned peaches."

The waiter informed them a moment later that the last of the peaches had been consumed by a squad of hungry merchants.

Dan and Leslie had stewed prunes for dessert.

CHAPTER XI

Masked Faces

THE slim, swift limousine sped through the silent, somehow friendly, darkness of the night. Wraiths of damp mist swept by like formless, clammy ghosts. There was little traffic and no sound except the ceaseless purr of the engine.

Now water glistened in the bright shafts of twin headlamps as the machine swung around a curve in the twining road, tires screeching over concrete. It crossed deserted prairie and wooded land and penetrated into lonely country where brooding darkness lay over undulating hills. Again rippling water lay ahead in lonely isolation. The big car skidded as its brakes were suddenly applied and slid to a stop.

Three men with black masks partially covering their faces stepped from the rear seat. The driver remained in the car.

"Here's the old water-filled gravel pit. We're at the right place." The gruff voice belonged to Con Sheldon.

Light from a pocket flashlamp spilled along

the ground. Somewhere an owl hooted mournfully and crickets sang their song of the night in the long grass. Outside the beam of the electric torch there was only blackness—complete, awesome.

Another voice was heard—the voice of Dave Dempster. "There's the house we're looking for!" He spoke in a hoarse whisper. "It's over there—on the other side of that clump of trees. See—there." He pointed in the darkness.

"You're right, Dave." Con Sheldon was elated. "I didn't think we'd find the house so easily. Now I see the lights myself."

Without further words they walked on through the darkness, following a poorly defined path through the thick underbrush. Vines tore at their clothes and leaves trailed across their faces. Swearing softly to himself, Con Sheldon brushed away hundreds of little swarming insects.

Riley, who had been in front, suddenly stopped. "We're at the house," he told them. "It's just beyond those big trees. I can see lights through the leaves."

"All set, men?" asked the leader.

"You bet," Riley assured him.

"We're ready, Con." The second assurance came from Dave Dempster himself.

"Fine. Now all we have to do is walk up to the door and knock. Get that. No rough stuff unless force is absolutely necessary. I'll give the signal if it is."

The three understood him perfectly. They nodded their heads in unison.

Con continued. "When we get inside, you, Riley, will cover whoever comes to the door after we knock—and anyone else in the room. Keep your gun out in plain sight. Let anyone around know you're dangerous. Dave and I will find Marston, the old railroad surveyor."

"I got yuh, chief."

Again they moved forward—this time at a much slower pace. Soon their heavy feet tramped on the stairs. Then they were on the porch of the house by the old gravel pit. Con Sheldon, still artfully masked, knocked heavily on a wooden outside door, and there was a noise within the house. Someone was coming to open it. The gangsters waited, tense—their guns drawn. They were ready for business—any kind of business.

The door swung open on creaky hinges. A young face stared out at them.

"Who's there?" The words were hoarse and frightened. They came in a husky, strained whisper. Eyes bulged in terror.

Con Sheldon went into action. His heavy fist

crashed upward. There was an ominous crack. The young man framed in the yellow of the lighted doorway pitched forward crazily. His body humped, slid to the floor. He lay still.

"There—there." There was a cruel satisfied note in the big man's voice. "He won't bother us, but watch him anyway, Riley. Come on inside, Dave. You and I have work to do."

The pair strode into the lighted room, leaving Riley in charge of their victim. From above came the heavy, questioning voice of another man— the voice of Marston, the railroad surveyor and track building expert.

"Come on, Dave," shouted Con Sheldon. "Let's get him!"

They pounded up the stairs, guns drawn. A door slammed above them and the vicious bark of a gun broke the stillness. The two invaders daringly flung themselves upward, hugging the sides of the stairway. Riley left the prostrate form of Con Sheldon's victim and leaped forward to help them, taking the stairs four at a time. His own gun pointed menacingly, ready for instant use.

Two shots rang out and then there was ominous silence.

———

"I'm really beginning to like this town," announced Dan. He was correcting advertising proof in the Clarion office and it was only the morning after his arrival in Norfolk.

"I'm really getting into things," he added.

Leslie Wysong gazed tranquilly over her typewriter at Dan's profile. As a profile it wasn't Greek perfection. Still it was a nice lively face, with strong features and expressive eyes.

"I'm glad you like us," she smiled. "I might add that we like you. The merchants are all talking about you. You made a splendid impression."

She changed the subject. "What are you doing this morning?"

"I'm going to call on a few of our advertisers first of all. Then I'm going to hire a car and run over to a place near Gosport. There's dirty work afoot there. But I expect to be back before your lunch hour. We'll eat again at Ptomaine Joe's poison inn."

"What has happened in Gosport?" Leslie questioned.

"Just this—an old geezer by the name of Marston was kidnapped near Gosport last night, and I think there's an important story connected with the abduction. And I'm going to read between the lines of that story!"

CHAPTER XII

The Blood Trail

DAN HYLAND stood looking up at the windows of the Marston house. Three hundred yards away the water, which almost completely filled the abandoned gravel pit, rippled in the clear, hard brightness of the early morning sunshine. The young man whistled a gay tune. He was back in his own "backyard" and he had hardly been in central Indiana for twenty-four hours! He was glad to be doing something familiar—glad to be police reporting again—glad to be playing an old game the rules of which he had practically invented for himself. He had covered Windy City crimes for three years while a member of the Chicago Daily Star staff, and now his first important story in Norfolk concerned a mysterious kidnapping!

Who had abducted Marston, the retired Chicago and Southern surveyor? Who had fired the shots in the night? Who had slugged Marston's son, Rudolph? Why had Marston been selected as a victim? What were the kidnapper's motives? The questions revolved dizzily in the young editor's head as he regarded the house on the pond with an interested stare. Time and future events would have to answer them for him.

Dan turned away from the mystery house, and his frank eyes met those of a deputy sheriff. Dan's grin was friendly and the officer glanced at his press pass and motioned an O.K.

He walked around the house. The sheriff and the state police were inside trying to find a clue to the identity of the kidnappers, but no clues seemed to be hanging around waiting to be pounced upon. Also Dan had received the impression after a brief acquaintance with the sheriff that that official had no great desire to discover clues or apprehend the abductors of old Marston. Craig, the sheriff, seemed to be merely going through the motions of conducting an investigation. Dan wondered why.

Rudolph Marston had told Craig that the kidnappers had taken him by surprise. Dan decided that they must have sneaked up to the house, coming up to it through the fields and shrubbery rather than by the road. Assuming his surmise was correct, the raiders must have returned the same way. They would hardly return by the road with their victim—especially if they were taking great pains to keep their identities a secret.

Dan left the house behind, heading toward the

thick shrubbery and the open field near the pond. The men who had carried Marston away in the night must have traversed the same general path, he thought. He moved forward more slowly when he came to the field, and then he suddenly came upon something which made his heart race with excitement. The grass at his feet was stained! He bent low and examined two or three of the marked blades. Then he gave vent to a low whistle of discovery. The dark brown stains, which contrasted queerly with the green of the grass, were blood stains.

He rose to his feet and placed three of the blades in an old envelope he had been carrying around in an inside pocket of his suit and began carefully to follow the trail which had been marked for him in human blood.

Con Sheldon was angry. He faced Corbin Watson across the now familiar round table in the secret meeting room of the ghost gang and shook his fist in the white, scared face of the smaller man. Watson was completely frightened.

"You poor, simple fool!" Sheldon raged. "You've done it now. I told you to watch young Hyland. And he runs off and butts in on the sheriff's investigating party at the Marston place."

"I *did* watch Hyland," the subject of Con's tirade defended weakly. "He got away from me. I guess he went out the back door of the Clarion office. There are two doors."

"I don't care if there are fifty doors. You should have watched them all! Now I'll have to take care of Hyland myself. He may have learned something. He can be dangerous to us."

"But what could I have done if I had seen him go out? I couldn't very well stop him, could I?"

"No—but you could have let me know so that I might notify Craig to keep him away from the Marston house and grounds."

"I'm sorry, boss." Watson groveled before him.

"You should be. Now I've got to watch out for young Hyland, unless I decide to put him out of the way until the danger's over. That may be the best plan."

"Any orders, Con?"

"Yes. Go to the new hide-out and find out how Marston is getting along. I fired two bullets at him last night after he took a wild shot at me. Neither of them hit him, but they scared him half to death and he fainted. The bullet he aimed at me grazed Dave Dempster in the arm and he bled like a stuck pig all the way back to the car. We had to carry Marston to the road."

"O.K., Con. I'll see how he is." Watson was anxious to redeem himself—eager to regain the favor of the evil, powerful general of a hundred dangerous criminals.

CHAPTER XIII

Danger in the Dark

LESLIE WYSONG looked up from correcting advertising proof as Dan noisily entered the Clarion office, emphatically slamming the door after him.

"What luck, Dan?" asked Leslie.

"I really accomplished something." He threw his hat on a pile of old papers and leaned against her desk. He spoke in a serious vein now, and Leslie looked up at him with interest.

"Really? Tell me all about your adventures."

"There's more between the lines of my story than in the actual narrative," he told her, "but I want you to hear it all, including my deductions and imaginings."

She put away the big proof sheets. "Go on, Mr. Editor."

"I got permission from the sheriff to inspect the Marston house," he began. "Craig and his men and a state policeman or two were handling the investigation. Rudolph, Marston's son, was on the scene, too. He's the young fellow the kidnappers slugged last night, before they carried off his father. Rudolph doesn't know a thing. He heard a knock and answered the front door. Masked men were on the porch. That's all he remembers. There's a black and blue spot on the end of his chin the size of a quarter."

Leslie shuddered. "How perfectly terrible," she exclaimed.

"Well, whoever socked Marston's son certainly swings a wicked right to the jaw. I'll say that much."

"Did you meet the sheriff, Dan?"

"Yes, I did, but he didn't impress me as being much of a defender of law and order. I've had a lot of experience around policemen, and Craig appeared to be merely going through the motions of conducting an investigation. His heart wasn't in his work, Les. I'm pretty sure of that."

"He's Con Sheldon's man, you know. Con may be influencing him in the Marston case. He has lots of underworld connections. I wish someone with power here in Norfolk could really get something on him—enough to send him to jail."

"Has it occurred to you that Con Sheldon might have planned this kidnapping?"

The girl's startled, surprised eyes clearly indicated that such an idea had never come to her.

"Wait a minute. I'm getting ahead of my

story, so I shouldn't have shot that question at
you."

She was more interested than ever now. He
went on with his surprising tale.

"Rudolph claims that a big man hit him. The
assailant also wore a mask to hide his identity.
Sheldon is a big man. Naturally Sheldon would
cover his face, if he went to Gosport to abduct
old Marston."

"But what motive could he possibly have for
taking part in such a crime, Dan?"

"You've got me there. Remember, I've only
been in Norfolk a short while. I'm not up on
all the gossip, scandal, and crime. Give me time."

"A big, masked man probably *did* hit Rudolph
Marston, but that's no proof Sheldon's guilty."

"All right, Les. I accept your point. We'll
leave Sheldon out of our story from now on.
Anyway, I prowled around in the house but
didn't learn much of importance. There were
signs of a struggle in Marston's bedroom, and
the old man's gun was on the rumpled bed. It had
evidently been dropped there. Only one chamber
had been emptied, although the neighbors near
the place claim they heard three shots. There
were many bloodstains on the stairway.

"I didn't learn anything more inside the house,
but outside, near the shrubbery surrounding the

grounds, I was able to pick up the bloodstained trail left behind by Marston, or whoever took him away. I followed those stains all the way to the seemingly little travelled road which serves the abandoned gravel pit. There I found automobile tire marks, which I sketched on paper, as they were rather peculiar. The crime car undoubtedly used that back road instead of the main highway. Somebody wasn't taking any chances on being seen."

"Did you follow the tire marks?"

"Yes—I did. I traced them back to where the side road joins the trunk highway. I lost them there."

"Fine work, Dan. Did you leave then?"

"Yes, I did. There seemed to be nothing else to stay for. I had all the necessary facts for my Clarion news story, so I came back to Norfolk."

"I hope you have a chance to check on those tire marks. Are they really very peculiar?"

He handed her a small sheet of paper; she pored over it for a full minute—then handed it back to him. "It *is* strange. Perhaps custom built or foreign tires made that design. Do you think so?"

"There's a chance that you're right. Anyhow, when I know people a little better in this burg, I'm going to do a little investigating among the tire dealers, filling station men, and garage mechanics. They may be able to trace this pattern. I copied it quite accurately."

"I hope they can help you, Dan."

"Those are my sentiments, too." He smiled thoughtfully. "You know, I'm not in much of a position at the present time to go snooping around attempting to solve kidnappings, so I'm going to stick to getting out my newspaper for the next few weeks. In other words, I'm going to sit tight and allow nature to take its course. For the next few days, at least, you'll find me an editor and publisher—and nothing else."

"What are you going to do right now?"

"We're going to lunch."

"——And after lunch?" she prompted.

"After lunch I'm going to write up my Marston kidnapping story for next week's paper—sticking directly to the facts. Then I'm attending a meeting of the Merchant's Association. Later on I'm planning to call on the mayor and other city officials. I expect to meet Sheldon at that time."

"——And tonight?" she persisted.

"Tonight I'm going to spend in strict solitude planning ways and means for putting my newspaper back on its feet. In another month we'll have the rival Post-Ledger yelling for mercy.

"I'm thinking about next week's issue, too. I'm going to distribute it free to every home in Norfolk, and I'm going to run a big front page editorial stating our new policy. From now on the Clarion is with the people and for the people. The decent element in this town can expect the utmost in co-operation from us, and I'm going to tell 'em so in big letters. Our next issue will go to everyone in town, and it'll really be important. And I'll follow it up with a subscription and advertising drive."

"Great, Dan! We'll get out a real paper next Friday!"

They were very sure of themselves.

The days passed on winged feet and turned themselves into weeks in an astonishingly short interval of time, and as the weeks flew by Dan Hyland's Norfolk Weekly Clarion became a great newspaper. Norfolk liked Ray Hyland's pleasant, fair, honest young nephew from the day of his arrival, and in surprisingly few weeks he was as much a part of the town as the water tower and old Grandpa Beggs, the venerable oldest inhabitant, who could remember the Lincoln and Douglas debates and the severe winter of eighteen hundred and eighty-four. But Norfolk's oldest inhabitant was content to live in the past; Dan Hyland lived in the present and in the future as well.

The Clarion, under Dan's editorship, came to life with a loud explosion; the loud explosion was the young editor's first editorial, printed in the first issue of the paper published under the new regime. A "new" Clarion was created—a Clarion impartial and fair to all—a Clarion that hired extra reporters and went out after advertising and subscriptions.

Dan Hyland promised the citizens of Norfolk a good newspaper. He gave them an excellent one. Circulation jumped a thousand copies in three weeks. The reasons—honest advertising, news, news, and then still more news and clever local features. Almost overnight the weekly changed from a skimpy four page paper to a well-filled eight page one. Dan hired reporters to cover church and club affairs; he personally covered official news and school events. A Clarion representative constantly canvassed the county, gathering personal news items and subscriptions. A peck of potatoes or a sack of grain could be exchanged for a year's subscription to the new Clarion. Ninety-seven "barter subscriptions" were secured, and Dan promptly turned all of the food collected over to the county relief agencies and his generous act was commended by every fair-minded person learning of it. The Clarion, quite modestly, said nothing of its owner's thoughtful generosity.

The Norfolk Clarion rapidly returned to its old top position. The Post-Ledger, never too well liked by the majority of citizens, found itself in an increasingly serious situation. The new, greater Clarion, however, was not built in a single week. Days, weeks of effort made it a great newspaper—moulded and formed by the honesty and sincere labor of Dan Hyland and Leslie Wysong.

In the first weeks of the paper's new existence, they worked side by side. Often lights burned until midnight in the editorial offices of the paper. Bringing the sheet back to its old position of high regard was a tremendous task. It was only accomplished because of the ceaseless toil of the young people. As new subscriptions dribbled and then poured in—as advertisers were won back to the Clarion one by one, they realized that their greatest reward would not come with mere financial success but would arrive with the triumphant realization that they had done a hard job well.

And so the Norfolk Clarion grew and prospered. It became an important part of Norfolk life. And the friendly Indiana city took the

Clarion's young editor to its large heart. Confidence in himself and in his adopted city and sincere hard work on his own part quickly made him one of Norfolk's most popular and respected citizens.

"Have you heard the news?"

Leslie Wysong's voice was swift and excited. She hurried into the Clarion inner office where Dan sat busily tapping at his battered old Underwood portable that had served him long and extremely well.

"Have you heard the news, Dan?"

"What news?" he grinned. "Say, young lady, you're really excited. Did a man bite a horse or has our little pal, Con Sheldon, broken a leg? What's up?"

"There has been another kidnapping, Dan! Wes Reid just telephoned the news from the police station."

"I'll be a son of a circus monkey! Give me the details." Dan leaned against his own desk for support, now fully as excited as his assistant.

"Here they are: A half hour ago four men in a black touring car kidnapped Frank Slauson. They picked him up near the Chicago and Southern station. He's a locomotive engineer. He runs the yard switch engine."

Breathless, Leslie stopped speaking.

"This kidnapping proves my theory," Dan informed her coolly. "Slauson and old Marston have been abducted because they know something about railroading. Marston is an old time railroad builder and surveyor; Slauson knows how to run an engine. The gang of criminals behind the three mail robberies are planning something new. Vance Murray hasn't bluffed them with his guards and inventor."

Leslie had a question. "Are you going to cover this story yourself? We've got to write something for this week's Clarion."

"You're right, as usual. But I can't do the yarn. I've something far more important than a news story to occupy my mind. Have Wes Reid write it. He's capable of pounding out good copy. This will be his big chance."

"All right. And what are you planning to do?"

"I've got to try to outguess the ghost gang, and I'm planning to hop the nine p.m. Chicago local. I want to have a talk with Vance Murray and his detectives."

"I'll carry on here until you return," Leslie promised loyally.

As the evening local jerked fitfully toward its destination, Dan had plenty of time to review in his mind the curiously significant twin kidnappings. He had the dimly lighted and ancient wooden coach all to himself. The progress made toward Chicago was exceedingly erratic and provokingly slow.

At eleven o'clock Dan fixed two of the faded red plush seats so that they faced each other and arranged his overcoat nicely over him and attempted to sleep, but the noise of the clattering cars and his own worried thoughts kept slumber away—denied him the rest he so much desired. In a few hours he would be in Chicago and somehow, someway he must contrive to see Vance Murray. As the train droned on, his restless mind planned for the future—working out a plan of action which might enable him to warn the Chicago and Southern of the great unknown danger ahead.

"Where's Slauson?"

The words were gruff and demanding. The man who spoke them dominated his rough surroundings. He was large, with a cruel face and little, piggish eyes. He was a complete tyrant.

"He's tied up."

The answer came from a short, poorly dressed man of middle age, whose unkempt beard straggled over an unnaturally pale face.

"Where?"

"In the back of this shack, boss."

"Does he know who seized him?"

"He hasn't said nothin'."

"Very well, Goris. Watch him closely. Nothing must go wrong now—understand?" The voice was ruthless. "My plans and preparations are nearly complete."

"Will you send me a message when you are ready for Slauson to play his part in our little show?"

"Yes, Goris. I will. The message will be in our code. Then you must bring your prisoner to the deserted farmhouse two miles from the Limedale railroad station. Bo Martino and some of the others will meet you there with a closed limousine, and they will have further instructions for you in writing. After you have read them, tear into bits the sheets on which they are written."

"O.K."

"——And bring Slauson to the farmhouse blindfolded. That is important."

"Is there anything else, Con?"

"No." Sheldon looked about him, taking in the rough unpapered walls of the shack. "Have you been bothered here?"

The man addressed as Goris shook his head negatively.

"That's great." Con Sheldon's heavy features twisted in a sinister grimace meant as a smile.

"If you're bothered, let Martino or Riley know. They'll send a guard, tough gorillas who shoot first and ask very few questions afterward."

Sheldon laughed at his own grim humor, and there was an almost demonic light in the little eyes.

CHAPTER XIV

Dan Turns Detective

UNKNOWN to his political allies and supporters, Con Sheldon had organized the ghost gang. A perfect organization, recruited from the best of Chicago and St. Louis gangdom, had enabled him to rob the Midnight Special on three occasions without detection. A wiser, less ambitious man would have known when to stop, but Sheldon's plans called for the opposite. His motto always was—"Go On. Push On." It became his personal creed, his philosophy of life.

He was about to carry out what he had described as "a little practical joke" not because it would particularly profit him to do so but because he wished to satisfy his own vanity by carrying a fantastic undertaking to a successful conclusion. Great risk and a possible loss of life meant nothing to him. He cared only for the gloating sense of power which completion would bring.

And so he was ready to risk everything to satisfy his own tremendous vanity. He had power. Now he wanted headlines—notoriety.

"Back already, Dan?"

Leslie Wysong smiled at her boss from the composing room doorway. She had returned from a consultation with Mike Ryan to find Dan humped over his own scarred desk and pounding rather viciously away at his typewriter.

"Yeah—I'm back." The words were spoken in a violent tone. Evidently he was not happy about something. The other two people in the room, a local reporter and an advertising lay-out man, who had been recently hired to help care for the growing needs of the paper, looked up from their own desks.

"Why the sorrow?"

"I'm not sad, Les. I'm laughing at myself for going up to Chicago and trying to mind someone else's business. My trip was a bust. I spent two nights and a day of good valuable time away from the paper for nothing."

"Just what do you mean?"

"Vance Murray told me to go roll my hoop."

Her voice and her smile were sympathetic. "I see."

"I had an old friend, Billy Parker, take me in to see Murray. I told him about the two kidnappings and how strange they were. I logically tied them up with the theft of the Kyle invention plans in Chicago, but Murray wouldn't listen. He just told me that he was prepared for trouble, and that the ghost gang would never be able to loot his trains again."

"And what did you say, Dan?"

"I didn't say anything. I left him, and then caught the Midnight Special."

"The next move——?"

He sighed. "I'm afraid you have me there."

Leslie feigned astonishment. "What! You haven't planned one?"

"I haven't had a chance to review the present situation here, and because I'm going to mind my own business, the Clarion's business, from now on, I'm not going to worry about the Chicago and Southern railroad and its troubles."

"I suppose you'd like to know what's been taking place around here? Or have you been informed?"

"Nope."

"Then I can supply the lacking information. The hue and cry over Slauson's disappearance has almost completely died down. There have been no ransom notes. The sheriff conducted a perfunctory investigation, aided by a handful of state police. They found nothing, and I don't believe Craig was much interested in learning anything. The Post-Ledger has been attempting to convince its readers that a Chicago gang abducted Slauson."

Don nodded wisely. "The ghost gang is playing the same old game. I only wish I were sure of Craig's connection with the gang. We at least know he's Con Sheldon's man."

Dan threw himself back in his old swivel chair and beckoned to the others in the office. "Gather 'round, staff, and keep what I have to say under your hats."

The local reporter and the lay-out man joined Leslie at Dan's battered desk. He had their complete attention, and as he spoke his words changed the impromptu gathering from a mere conference to a council of war.

"There's going to be another railroad robbery," Dan pronounced solemnly, "and it's going to make the previous three lootings look small and unimportant."

Leslie protested. "But there hasn't been a hold-up on the Chicago and Southern for weeks and weeks. There are guards on the trains, and the new protective invention has been installed in some of the mail and through baggage cars carried by the Midnight Special."

"You're right," agreed Dan, "but I still say there's going to be a robbery—and soon too. I tried to warn Vance Murray in Chicago yesterday with no success."

"Why do you think the robberies aren't over yet, Dan?"

"That's simple, Les. Why do you suppose two unsolved kidnappings have taken place here recently—abductions involving Chicago and Southern men in both instances?"

"I haven't an answer for that one, Mr. Detective."

"Well, I have, gal. Those men were kidnapped because of their railroad connections! That much is clear because no ransom has been asked and because neither victim had an enemy in the world. Marston was an old railroad surveyor. He knows this section of the country well—especially the particular sections crossed by Chicago and Southern tracks. Slauson, the engineer, knows the right-of-way like a book. They both would prove very useful to a gang planning a perfect train robbery."

"I'm beginning to see things your way, Dan." It was Leslie who spoke. The others were hanging on the young editor's every word with rapt attention.

"Vance Murray failed to see any connection between the kidnappings and the Chicago and Southern robberies, past or future. He steadfastly sticks to the belief that a Chicago gang of hoodlums is responsible for all the trouble. He almost laughed at me when I told him I was convinced that a gang operating in central Indiana looted the Special and is planning a new coup.

"I'm not going to bother longer with the Chicago and Southern. If they want to take chances with the Midnight Special, they won't find Dan Hyland minding their business. From now on I'm playing detective solely for the benefit of my newspaper. The Clarion will reap any rewards which may come through my sleuthing. Three lootings have already taken place and two local men have been abducted. Next week the extra guards will be taken off the Midnight Special. The mysterious Lucian Kyle invention and a handful of men will be left to watch over valuable postal and money shipments. The plans for the Kyle invention were stolen weeks ago, so the gangsters must be prepared to meet its threat."

Dan paused for effect, watching the others. He could tell by the varied expressions on their faces that they believed in him—that they knew he was right.

"So from now on we're working for the Clarion. All that has passed—the kidnappings, the previous hold-ups, and the none too interested attitude of the sheriff in the abduction cases, leads me to believe that something big, more than likely another huge mail robbery, will take place on the Chicago and Southern in this part of the state. We're going to be ready and waiting for such an event. The Clarion is going to be ready for trouble and, if it comes, we're going to be ready to offer a solution of the crimes to the people of Indiana and to the railroad detectives. The Clarion must expose the men who have been robbing the Midnight Special."

Leslie Wysong was smiling a little. "Those are noble words, Dan."

"Certainly they're noble, and they are also serious."

Sunlight streamed through a rather grimy windowpane, undaunted. It spilled over the ancient boards of the Clarion office floor; it made life warm and bright and comfortable. Trouble and livid banners of flame spitting into black emptiness from noisy, death laden bandit guns seemed far away. Paul Revere, the office cat, lay on his back lazily enjoying his morning sun bath. Paul Revere snored a little, and his furry black legs twitched as he dreamed of capturing a mouse.

"I'm going to return to the detective business," said Dan. "I'm going to begin operations by attempting to trace the tire marks I copied from the little-used side road near Marston's house. Then I'm going on from there. If the local authorities aren't interested, I am."

"The paper is doing well now, Dan. You can afford to take time off for your sleuthing."

"I suppose I can, Les, and if we can expose the gang which has been responsible for the Chicago and Southern's troubles, the Clarion will reap the glory."

The girl's eyes gleamed with anticipation. The newspaper had already travelled far along the road to complete recovery. A great public service performed by the Clarion's editor and the paper itself would mean success and fame beyond their wildest dreams.

The four in the office heard sudden, heavy footsteps in the street. Then the shrill squeak of the opening office door broke the quiet of the drowsy morning. Startled from his mouse hunt, Paul Revere bounded off toward the composing room. The four in the office turned toward the door as one person.

The visitor was Con Sheldon. He stood in the entrance way wearing what was intended as a disarming, guileless smile.

CHAPTER XV

A Strange Visitor

IT CAN never be said of Con Sheldon that he did not know how to meet expertly a delicate situation. Through a canny trick of personality he could usually manage to clear the most hostile air. He knew that none of the four liked him—all would gladly have seen him behind prison bars. Secretly he hated them because they were between him and the victory he coveted so much. But as he stood in the enemy's camp, his manner was friendly, affable—suspiciously so, Dan thought.

"Busy, Hyland?" The words purred softly.

"No, I'm not. Did you want to see me?" Dan's voice was distant and business-like. The three others were on the sidelines, watching the play being enacted before them.

The "big boss" was quite a distinguished figure in the well cut gray clothes he always affected. His voice was still of the smooth quality, but his cold eyes swept the room like an Arctic blast. He was cool, competent, conscious of his power.

"I *do* want to see you, Hyland."

"Come in and sit down, won't you?" Dan was being very polite.

The big head shook, but the professional smile still slightly tempered the hard cruelty of the well known Sheldon features. Con declined a chair.

"No—I won't sit down."

Leslie and the other two hastily excused themselves. They all suddenly remembered urgent business in the composing room and disappeared. Dan was left alone with his unlooked for visitor. They could now talk man to man. The sunlight still streamed through the office windows but its sleepy friendliness had disappeared. To Dan the air seemed charged with a strange, exciting electricity.

"No need of any preamble," said Sheldon. "You know why I'm here." He propped his big body against a high proof table. His fat, well manicured hands moved restlessly.

"I'm afraid you're wrong, Mr. Sheldon," Dan answered suavely.

"Wrong? Why?"

"Because I don't know why you're here."

The great head tossed impatiently. The professionally pleasant manner was rapidly disappearing.

"You're not dumb, youngster. You know why

I walked in here this afternoon." The smile became a knowing leer.

"I'm still afraid I don't know what you're driving at. I know who you are, and I know your position in this town and county. We've met casually several times during the past few weeks, but I'm still in the dark as to the motives behind your call."

"O.K. I'll explain." The announcement was brusque.

"Fine. Now we're not wasting each other's time."

Sheldon decided to overlook the direct thrust. The old professional smile returned as he began to talk.

"You've been printing some pretty nasty things about me, Hyland."

"They've been true."

"We won't argue that now." Sheldon was keeping his unruffled, affable composure with some difficulty.

"Argument isn't necessary, Sheldon. The Clarion has the truth and real facts on its side."

The big man overlooked the interruption. As he went on, his voice was placating.

"There's no reason why we can't be friends, Hyland. You know my position here. You admitted as much. You're new in Norfolk, and perhaps I can help you in some way."

"You're right. I *am* a newcomer, and I've also learned the ropes in a surprisingly short length of time. I've learned that the honest people in this town can't trust you and your crowd."

Sheldon snapped a warning.

"Better be careful. Watch what you're saying!"

"I'll be careful when it serves my interests. Just why did you really come here to see me?"

"I don't like what you've been printing about me in your paper. Speaking frankly, I'm here to buy you out. I'll give you more than a fair price for the Clarion in return for full control.

"I suppose you will." Dan grinned. His anger was gone and a feeling of triumph had taken its place. Con Sheldon wanted to buy him out! The man's own offer indicated that he feared the Clarion—feared the forces of right and justice which it represented.

"You'll sell then?" Sheldon leaned forward eagerly.

Dan shook his head, still grinning.

"No?" The eagerness changed to surprise, then chagrin.

"The Norfolk Weekly Clarion is not for sale, Sheldon."

"That your final answer?"

"It is."

"You're being very foolish."

"I think not. Naturally, our opinions can hardly be alike."

The thick lips curled cruelly. All friendly pretense was gone from the face now. Con Sheldon stood unmasked before the young man who was soon to become his greatest enemy.

"You may be willing to *give* me your newspaper in a few days! I've done my part and I'm through. I've offered to buy you out. You've had your chance to make an exit from Norfolk gracefully and with money in your pockets. Before many days have passed you'll make your exit— *but not gracefully*. Remember that, Mr. Smart Guy Editor."

Although Sheldon was reddening with anger because of the defiance thrown in his face, Dan remained cool and grinning.

"You'll hear from me again," Con exploded savagely. "I don't like you; I don't like your paper. I'll ruin you."

"Good afternoon, Mr. Sheldon," Dan spoke with mocking suavity.

The words were unnecessary. He had already stormed out of the office.

"Don't slam the door," Dan laughed after him as a crash reverberated through the office.

Leslie Wysong came swiftly from the composing room, her face a picture of alarm and concern.

"Oh, Dan, he's awful. I was listening—heard every word he said, and now he's going to make trouble for you." The words tumbled out one after another. She was excited, afraid for the young man who was her employer and friend.

"I'm not worrying about Sheldon," Dan informed her. "He's obviously afraid of us, and I think I know why. He more than likely knows that I contacted Vance Murray in Chicago. He probably thinks I warned the Chicago and Southern president against him."

"He threatened you."

"So he did, and I'm convinced now that he's connected with the ghost gang. I must prove my conviction and put Sheldon behind the bars before he can make trouble for me."

CHAPTER XVI

Flaming Guns

DUSK was falling when Dan left the Clarion office for Ptomaine Joe's place and his evening meal. He still lived at the Norfolk House but had fallen into the habit of eating most of his meals at Joe's little restaurant.

Dan locked the office door. Leslie Wysong and the other Clarion staff members had deserted the building long ago. They had left him sitting at his desk, still turning over in his mind the threatening words Con Sheldon had spoken that morning.

Dan heard a noise. He turned and a masked figure sprang out at him from the shadows. A heavy fist swung upward and smashed into his face. Reeling, he staggered back against the door and slumped to the ground, almost unconscious. He heard retreating footsteps. His attacker was running away.

He lay still for a long time before struggling to his feet. Picking up his hat, he discovered that a plain white envelope had been concealed beneath it. He gingerly rubbed his sore jaw and poked an exploring finger into the envelope. It brought forth a slip of paper. Even in the semi-darkness he could read the message, which had been written with a black crayon.

He unlocked the door and went inside the office. Turning on lights, he read the message again and again—his head aching. This was war!

HYLAND—GET OUT OF TOWN OR WE'LL KILL YOU!

THE GHOST GANG.

The words were a challenge. Dan carefully put it away in his desk. Then he went into the washroom, where he dusted off his clothes and washed his face.

Dan again left the Clarion office, once more locking the door. This time he was not bothered as he left the building.

His mind was in a whirl. What was the next move? He must strike at Con Sheldon—but how? Sheldon had fired the first gun. Now he must return the fire or lose his battle. He knew that the ghost gang would kill him if he stood in their way. Slowly Dan moved down the street toward his dinner.

An electric lamp of modest candle power burned at the corner, feebly illuminating a few square feet of ancient concrete sidewalk. He crossed the roadway and walked along a path half hidden by a mass of fresh green leaves. A chill evening wind blew through the stout branches of massive trees. The side street was lonely and forlorn in the night shadows.

Dan came to another corner and left his path and turned off on another side street, a block away from Main. His feet left rustling leaves for crunching gravel. He passed a few dark, mean buildings—a tin shop and an old livery stable, now a second rate garage. He came to Main street, almost deserted at that hour of the evening, and again crossed the pavement, threading his way between automobiles parked along the curbing. On the wide seat of a shoe shining stand three farmers lolled at ease, and regarded him with mild interest as he went on toward his brightly lit goal.

"Evenin', Hyland."

"Good evening, Bixby." He greeted Zack Bixby, who was standing in front of his small grocery indulging in a fragrant dinner hour pipe.

"It's a nice paper you're printing these days, young fellow. I subscribed two weeks ago."

Thanking the merchant for the compliment, Dan went on. A hundred feet farther on behind a great unwashed plate glass window he found

Ptomaine Joe's "poison inn" dispensing its cheer and dubious nutrition. A high lunch counter and a wide, grimy mirror running the length of the room suggested that in damper days the place had been something more than a restaurant.

The boy climbed on to one of the perilously high stools. At his right, far too close for comfort, sat an unkempt man in greasy overalls, with a two days' growth of beard on his lean face. A glance to the left was all that was necessary to cause Dan to shout with joy. Billy Parker was seated beside him.

"Billy Parker! You scoundrel! What are you doing in Norfolk?"

The well dressed young man on the stool at his left swung around, a grin spreading over his face.

"Dan! I didn't expect to find you so soon. I arrived on the afternoon train from Chicago. I thought I'd get a bite to eat and then look you up at your hotel."

"It's swell to see you. How come you're in town, fellow?"

"I'll explain when we're alone, Dan. I can't talk here. Where can we talk, pal?"

"In my room—at the hotel."

"So you're glad to see me, eh?" Billy Parker

grinned and rested his rather large feet on his friend's bed.

"I'll say I am!"

"Well, if there's a chance of excitement somewhere, you'll find Billy Parker hanging around right on the spot."

"But how did Gargan happen to allow you to come chasing down here, Mr. Reporter? Explain."

"After you left me yesterday in Chicago, I went in to see the big boss. I repeated carefully for his benefit everything you told me about the kidnappings and this guy Con Sheldon. After I finished he decided that there was likely to be more trouble in this area, so I'm here, bag and baggage, ready to cover anything which may come up in the way of important news."

"I catch on. Gargan thinks I'm right about the kidnappings."

"He doesn't think you're right about anything. He's merely protecting the paper in case big news breaks in this vicinity. He's placing me here for a few days so that the Star will be in a swell position to scoop all the other Chicago papers if a big news yarn pops up."

"Gargan's wise, Billy."

"Sure, he's wise."

"Something is going to happen around here—

and soon, too. Con Sheldon, the political boss, visited me this morning. It seems that I've been printing nasty things about him and he wants to buy me out."

"You refused his offer?"

"Of course, Billy. And, when I did, he threatened me—said I'd better be a good boy or watch out for goblins."

"Nice little playmate, Sheldon. I hope he didn't succeed in scaring you, Dan."

"He didn't. But just the same I'm watching my step from now on. If I walk into trouble, I'll take the stroll with my eyes wide open."

"I think something really *is* going to happen around Norfolk." Billy was completely serious now. "I'm glad I came. We can work together now. Even if we can't prevent disaster, we can at least be right on hand—ready for trouble."

"Attaboy, Billy! We're working together again. You are here for the Star, and I'm the Clarion's 'Johnny-on-the-Spot.' The old team of Parker and Hyland is re-united!"

The laboring engine cleared the Limedale interlock tower and clattered over a double cross-over. Then flanged wheels bit into steel as the train rolled around a well banked curve, playing follow the leader only to straighten out in a long line short moments later.

Gaining momentum with every turn of its drivers, Engine 3011 settled down to the exacting task of hauling the heavy Midnight Special. A green semaphore light changed to yellow and on to red as the Special flashed past.

Down grade now! The big drivers spun like electric fans and the man in the engineer's seat strained forward and opened his throttle wide. His fireman yanked at the whistle cord, and a lamenting wail drowned out the clacking of the car wheels and the staccato bark of the exhaust. Green lights, white lights, and furious red lights plunged by.

Outside the car windows was a glaze of darkness splotched with the gold of infrequent mysterious lights. In lighted mail cars busy clerks sorted mail as if their very lives depended upon the speed of nimble and accurate fingers.

And far ahead of the swift Midnight Special, far from the pounding drivers and howling whistle, Con Sheldon barked orders. Gangsters grew tense and nervously fingered their guns. All was ready!

The Midnight Special penetrated the factory district of a small city. Furnaces spurted flame and power hammers were clanging. Scarlet and orange fire licked at cadaverous stacks, at brick walls and sullen, motionless machines and con-

verters. There was a sliding silhouette of trees
and village lamps that stood against the dark
like exclamation points.

Clear board! Nothing can stop the Midnight
Special from rushing to its doom.

Grim faced men lined up along the Chicago
and Southern right of way, men with lean, hard
features—dangerous, daring men. They were all
members of Con Sheldon's augmented gang, and
they had been armed with machine guns and
high-powered rifles. Still other members of the
gang sat in swift cars near two little-used grade
crossings. They too were armed.

Con Sheldon was ready for action—crouched
and ready to spring. He was prepared to make a
dramatic bid for notoriety, directing his little
army of evil from a secret cove.

Dan and Billy, unaware of the approach of a
momentous event, sat in Dan's hotel room discussing the problems confronting the publisher
of a weekly newspaper, and old Vance Murray
slept peacefully in Chicago, secure in the belief
that Lucian Kyle's invention would protect his
pet train from robbery.

George Brandon moved a long lever and a
manual block signal two hundred yards from
Tower XY dropped from "caution" to "clear."
The alert towerman pulled another of the many

handles before him and released a spring derail. Four hundred feet to the south of the tower the main line of the St. Louis and Indiana railroad crossed the Chicago and Southern. It was the duty of the towerman at XY to prevent possible accidents at the cross-over. When a C and S train approached, Brandon set his signals against anything which might be on the St. Louis and Indiana rails. When both lines were clear, all signals were kept at the stop position and were changed just before the arrival of trains.

George Brandon was a careful man and knew his job. As a result C and S trains never crashed into those on the other road. The towerman glanced at the clock built into his electric signal control panel. In ten minutes he would "clear" the Midnight Special. He had set his signals and was ready for the train. In nine minutes the Special's headlight would herald its approach. Then would come the rattle of a mighty steel monster, and almost before he knew it the train would sweep by the little box-like house set on long stilt "legs" to thunder over the crossing plates and on into the darkness.

Brandon glanced toward the neat line of railroad lanterns near the door and then at his battery of signal and derail levers. A ticking telegraph instrument reported to his trained ear the important fact that the Special had cleared Tower LN. Another eight or nine minutes would bring it to XY.

The night was a cool one and Brandon had started a fire in the tower's rusty barrel stove. A single light bulb glowed over the long battery of levers and electric switches. The tiny equipment-filled room was a little world in itself—a world which Brandon knew well. A small but important cog in the machinery of a great railroad, he played his part with expert ease. He awaited the Special with his usual complete composure. Years of experience had made the arm which pulled the signal controls sure and steady, and now he was ready for the train—his preparations finished. A clear board would allow Vance Murray's pride and joy to flash past the tower and over the crossing—on time.

Brandon gazed reflectively out of the tower's front windows. Below him the twin rails gleamed faintly in the pale light cast by switch marker lamps. And then suddenly he realized with a start that he was not alone in the semi-darkness. Unknown menace lurked in the shadows.

George Brandon's heart leaped within him; he stepped away from the wide windows and whirled to face the masked faces of three roughly dressed men. Two of the trio covered him with big revolvers; the other gave curt orders.

"Put up yer hands, Brandon!" The voice was rough and cold.

The towerman raised his hands and backed slowly toward the signal controls behind him.

"Leave them handles alone. We don't wantcha to change nothin' until we give yuh orders. Get that!"

Brandon stood very still, waiting for his unwanted visitors to make the next move. An order was not long in coming.

"Sit down in that chair by the trap door."

The prisoner obeyed, still silent, while the unarmed one of the three produced a small coil of rope from under his coat and stepped toward him.

"Bind him, Mo. I'll hold your baby cannon." The leader handed the rope to one of his men and looked on as Brandon was quickly and strongly bound to the wooden chair.

"Now gag him, Mo."

The man addressed as Mo finished his work and stepped back to view his labors. The other two patted him on the back and their hard laughter filled the room—cruel mockery in the ears of the unfortunate towerman.

After he had carefully checked Mo's work,

the leader found the time in which to explain his forceful presence.

"We sneaked up through the trap door when your back was turned, Brandon. We got our orders and we don't aim to hurt you—see. The three of us are going to play signal tower-man for a little while, until after the Special goes through. We like to play railroad games."

Brandon was forced to remain on the sidelines and watch helplessly as two more masked men came up through the trap door and worked at the signal controls in complete silence. Not another word was spoken. Even the usually garrulous telegraph ticker was still for the moment. He watched them shift levers—watched the block signal indicator waver and finally change from green to red. The masked invaders were closing the block against the Midnight Special! They planned to stop the train at Tower XY.

Their work accomplished, four of the five left the tower, disappearing through the hole in the floor and leaving but one of their number to guard George Brandon. From below came the low rumble of many harsh voices. A red signal light and a derail were set against the expected Midnight Special, and now the hoarse whistle and rattle of a train could be heard in the early morning stillness.

Engine 3011 thundered up grade toward Pleasantville and Tower XY. The long line of cars swept along like a tornado but as smoothly as an expensive limousine. Fallen leaves and dust rose up in a great unsteady wall behind the Midnight Special and flowers and grasses on the banked right of way waved and tossed. Passengers sitting in the club car viewed only rushing darkness, and as the train darted down a line of freight cars, the noise of the moving cars re-echoed with a crashing sound like that of falling buildings. Engine 3011 bellowed like a mad fiend and rushed on as though bent on immediate destruction.

In the local mail car directly behind the engine busy clerks sorted mail with lightning speed and a mail clerk stood constantly at the car's side door—ready to raise his catcher hook and spear a full sack of mail out of the night. The half-clothed clerks moved about in desperate haste, and every car wheel hummed. The engine seemed like a wild steed that now could not be controlled by the engineer. Volleys of sparks shot up from the chimney as though from the mouth of a cannon. The bright lights shone out on each side of the cars against a curtain of black which rolled backward. In the darkness the mail clerk on duty at the "catcher" fully expected to catch a freight car on a siding or a bridge upright. In the open doorway nothing could be seen but a shower of sparks and the dim marker light on the mail crane ahead. With a deafening crash, the fat bag of mail from Pleasantville suddenly struck the upraised catcher and bounded into the mail car. The engineer ahead was a tiny mite to govern the monster of steel and iron he rode upon. He was a mere insect compared with the man-made steed whose fierce energy he controlled.

The Midnight Special flashed on through Pleasantville, a confused perspective of dark houses, empty freight cars, and dim lights.

Far ahead of the flying 3011 a yellow signal light gleamed as a silent warning. Slow block ahead! The engineer and fireman leaned outward anxiously. Their orders, handed to them at La-Fayette, had contained nothing to indicate other than clear track ahead. The veteran at the throttle shrugged his shoulders and checked the engine. His fireman finished stoking and climbed to his rough, precarious perch on the left side of the bulging boiler. The big drivers slowed, revolving with greater leisure as they slipped under the yellow signal. Engineer Bert O'Malley was obey-

ing orders, and 3011's whistle shrieked question-
ingly.

In the registered mail car the clerks and two
guards went about their business confidently. Did
not Lucian Kyle's famous "electric eyes and
ears" guard their precious charge? And in the
through baggage car a lone armed baggageman
sat before the burglar proof safe which contained
the Chicago and Southern railroad's Louisville
pay roll money.

Gleaming track slipped beneath the heavy
driving wheels of the Special's engine; the thrusts
of the twin piston shafts became more leisurely.
A brakeman in the rear of the observation car
stepped out on the wide platform, red lantern in
hand. The telegraph poles beside the right of
way, which a few moments before had seemed
one continuous picket fence, passed in review in a
more stately procession now, for Bert O'Malley
had cut the speed of his train in half. Engine
3011's pilot wheels rolled around a sharp, well
banked turn. Ahead the track was straight for
a full five hundred yards, and at the end of the
steel straightaway a red signal light shone
ominously against the starry pattern of the sky.

Red for danger!

The Midnight Special faced a closed block,
while Con Sheldon's lawless men lurked in the

darkness. 3011's big whistle moaned and air
hissed through the brake lines. Brake shoes
clamped against slowing wheels. Clanking and
rattling like a live thing, the big engine and its
long train jerked to a halt and for a brief moment
only the roar of escaping steam broke the stillness. Con Sheldon had halted the Midnight
Special.

Then came the attack. Guns blasted.

Armed men swarmed out of the gloom—
dangerous men armed with machine guns and
heavy duty automatic revolvers and shot guns.
Banners of livid flame spat into the chill early
morning. As an army of bandits swarmed over
the engine and mail and baggage cars, other
members of the gang appeared along the right
of way and climbed aboard the Pullmans at the
end of the train. While five of the daring ghost
gang boarded the engine and overcame O'Malley
and the fireman, another group were hailing
bullets at the treasure laden mail and baggage
cars which were behind the locomotive. Red and
blue ribbons of flame curled viciously—flared
against the ebony curtain of darkness. Con Sheldon, who had planned and plotted, watched from
behind a protecting boulder. He, too, was masked
and dressed in sombre black. His acute sense of
the dramatic and sensational had even dictated

his choice of costume. His own gun spat livid fire as he saw a luckless trainman attempting to escape toward a nearby farmhouse. His victim lurched forward, then fell to the hard rock of the Chicago and Southern roadbed—his valiant effort to secure help a failure. A cruel grin replaced the grim frown on the countenance of the leader.

All was now confusion. Passengers were herded from the train and lined up in a long shivering row beside the tracks, but no attempt was made to enter the registered mail car and the baggage compartment containing the pay roll money! The bandits swarmed about the cars and over them, staying carefully away from the doors behind which the handful of mail clerks were prepared to make a last heroic stand. They were ready to die like heroes—ready to protect their precious charge with their lives. And still no attack was launched upon the treasure cars. What strange method could possibly be behind Con Sheldon's seeming madness? What surprise would be sprung next?

One was not long in coming. While the gangsters hidden behind rocks and in the tall grass continued to hurl leaden death at the steel cars, all of the passengers and train crew were forced out of the Pullmans and coaches of the Special.

Bert O'Malley and his fireman were dragged from the engine and made to join the cold, miserable prisoners along the trackside. A blindfolded figure was boosted into the cab. The unwilling new engineman was Slauson, the victim of the Norfolk station abduction of a few days before! One of the ghost gang had prepared himself to play fireman, and while Slauson was being placed on the engineer's seat, he picked up a handy shovel and began to stoke 3011's roaring fire.

The next surprise arrived only a short moment later. Half of the bandit gang jumped aboard the train as a sort of renegade train crew, leaving but eight or nine of their number behind to guard the regular train crew and passengers. With the exception of the mail clerks and baggagemen the entire Midnight Special was now manned by Con Sheldon's men, and a blindfolded engineer sat at 3011's throttle! The men in the baggage and mail cars were barricaded and trapped on the train, and inside the registered mail car Lucian Kyle's protective invention photographed and recorded futilely. Quite suddenly the outlaw firing ceased and all was still—for a brief ten seconds. For those ten seconds there was only the innocent music of the crickets chirping merrily—harmless little creatures who were not aware that something terrible was taking place.

Con Sheldon stepped from behind his sheltering rock and strode toward the engine. He waved a dark gloved hand, and in answer to his signal armed men hoarsely whispered instructions to the trembling man at the throttle. A gun was thrust into his back. The locomotive's whistle shrieked twice; steam hissed from open valves and there was a whistling sound as the air brakes on each car were released.

Mighty drivers spun and bit into the steel. The train groaned forward with a farewell volley of rocketing sparks. The eight men guarding the prisoners, led by Con Sheldon, jumped aboard the observation platform at the last minute, still covering the train crew and passengers with their guns. The signal light ahead changed to "clear" and the Special clattered over the cross-over plates—away from the scene of the most amazing abduction ever staged. The ghost gang had kidnapped an entire train, treasure, guards, and Pullmans, and was running it to suit themselves. They could now loot it at leisure. The bewildered, frightened, and completely miserable victims of Con Sheldon's clever scheming remained where the bandits had herded them, forlorn and alone.

The Midnight Special roared on into the secretive dark to become a baffling mystery. The warning lights on the end of the train were soon tiny pin points of dull red in the distance that soon flickered out.

Somewhere between Tower XY and Norfolk the Midnight Special suddenly vanished from the face of the earth.

CHAPTER XVII

Baffling Mystery

WRAPPED in gloom, Dan Hyland sat before his desk in the Clarion office, staring dismally at a much marked paper before him. For ten minutes he had drawn absently on that paper, and there was an unusual air of discouraged preoccupation about him which was quite understandable in the light of recent events. It was very early, and Dan had the office to himself. Paul Revere slept soundly beneath Wes Reid's desk.

He did not mind the temporary isolation; in fact, he rather enjoyed it. Soon the rest of the staff would arrive and he would be alone with his thoughts no longer.

The abduction of the Midnight Special, but little more than an hour before, had left him weak—hanging on the ropes, as Billy would have put it. A telegraph messenger had brought the news from the station and the night hotel clerk had roused him. Dan and Billy had dashed breakfastless to the station where a few more meagre facts were learned. The station agent had repeated over and over again to all questioners: "She hasn't showed up here. She hasn't showed up here." Dan had left Billy at the station to cover later developments. Norfolk, even at dawn, was beginning to buzz with excitement. Dan felt cross and futile.

A telephone bell tinkled and the young editor reached for the instrument, wearily speaking into the mouthpiece. Sleep was still in his eyes; his shirt was only half buttoned, and his tie hung unknotted around his neck. He was waiting impatiently for Billy Parker to return so that they might together formulate a plan of action.

"Hello. Clarion office. Hyland speaking."

An answering voice came over the wire. Dan's tired face brightened perceptibly.

"Good morning, Les. Where are you anyway?"

There was a pause while Dan listened, then he spoke again. "Oh, I see. You're at your brother's place. Well, finish your breakfast and hurry over here. There's lots to be done. Besides, I want to talk to you. Yes, it's true—incredible but true. They woke me up at dawn to give me the bad news. The entire train is missing.

"I've been down here for a half hour alone, trying to think of some plan of action."

There was a click at the other end of the wire as the connection was broken, and Dan put his own receiver back on its hook. As he pushed the instrument away Billy Parker bounded noisily into the office, slamming the outside door behind him.

"Hello, Old Man Gloom. Had your breakfast yet?"

"No, Billy."

"Come on then. I haven't had mine."

"I don't feel like eating right now. Instead, I want to talk with you."

"All right, Dan, but banish the sad look of mourning from your usually pleasant face. This great railroad mystery isn't our funeral, pal."

"I suppose not, but I'm sad just the same," his friend retorted shortly.

"—And I know why you're wearing a long face, Mr. Small Town Editor-turned-detective. You are a picture of gloom because the ghost gang has forced your hand. Before this morning you were all ready to settle down to a little private party at which you and you only would have the privilege of playing hide and seek with the men who have been robbing Vance Murray's pet train—the smart lads who stole the engine and cars early this morning. You're a little bit mad because the eyes of the country are now turned on Norfolk. Your party isn't private any longer. Before nightfall this town will be filled with detectives and big city newspaper men. It'll be as popular as Coney Island on a hot Sunday."

"You're right, Billy."

"Sure, I'm right. Now the question is—what are you going to do about this nice little mystery which has been dumped right into your lap? Are you going out and run down the ghost gang before the detectives and newshawks have a chance to arrive on the scene, or are you going to lie down on the job—quit merely because what happened this morning has forced you to share your little pet detective project with the rest of the world?"

Billy Parker knew the answers to his own questions almost before he had finished speaking. Dan had squared his shoulders, and once more the light of battle flamed in his eyes.

"I'm going out and get the ghost gang, Billy, and you're going to help me! We're not going to rest until we have solved the mystery of the Midnight Special! And we're going to bring to justice the men who have robbed the train! Vance Murray's pride and joy disappeared into thin air somewhere between Tower XY and Norfolk. Billy, we're going to find that train, and we're going to find the men who kidnapped it!

Dan looked around him at the expectant faces of Leslie Wysong and Billy Parker and began to speak. He straightened up in his chair, and his body as well as his voice was charged with vitality.

"We're beginning a real battle this morning," he told them. "This Midnight Special mystery is exactly what the doctor ordered to finish putting the Clarion back on the map—once and for all. We're going to get the jump on the police and the other papers by going out ourselves and solving the big mystery. We'll capture the ghost gang on the side! Can't you see the headlines now —*Clarion editor solves mystery; finds missing train; captures notorious train robbers?* What a service to the community that would be!"

"Are you mad, Dan?" asked Leslie Wysong.

"I may be. To tell the truth, I'm not sure but what *I am* crazy, but it's sink or swim now—and we've got to swim and we're going to swim. That's that."

"Attaboy, Dan," applauded Billy. "If you're crazy, I want to be crazy too."

"Well, I might as well join you lunatics," Leslie sighed. "You outnumber me two to one, and your enthusiasm is contagious. Lead on."

"Now that we're all together, I'll outline a plan of action for the next few hours," began Dan. "Here goes:

"First of all, we're going to have action—plenty of it. Leslie, you will be in charge of the Clarion. You're going to advertise the news that the Clarion will solve the mystery of the missing train. You're going to shout to the world that we're out to capture the ghost gang. Run the big news in black headlines—*Clarion to perform great public service*. You're going to let the ghost gang know we're after them.

"Billy and I are going out after the train and the gang. We're gambling everything on our ability to make good the promises you'll shout in the Clarion. This is our great opportunity—our chance for a fight to a finish with Con Sheldon. I'm convinced that he's mixed up in this sorry mess in some way. I'm going to prove my convictions to the world. If I fail, the Clarion goes down to defeat with colors flying; if I win I'll have beaten Con Sheldon once and for all.

"The success of our entire plan depends upon speed, hard work, and good luck. Les, you are to get out an extra edition right away. Shout the word from the housetops! The Clarion is going to find the Midnight Special; the Clarion, performing the greatest public service ever conceived, will capture the men behind the robberies and the disappearance of the train!"

"I get you, Dan. We're out for blood." The girl was now thoroughly enthusiastic. "I'm with you heart and soul. I'll get out an extra which will scream the news—an extra that will be the talk of the town. You *must* make good."

"We're leaving the office now," he told her, "and we won't rest or give up until the ghost gang is behind the bars. We won't give up until the mystery has been solved. I'm staking everything —gambling my all on success."

"We're going to bring 'em back alive!" shouted Billy.

"Suppose you fail?" Leslie asked slyly.

"We're not going to fail." Dan pounded on the desk. "There can be no 'ifs'—no failure. Failure means ruin."

The three jumped up from the conference, ready for action. The battle was on! War was declared, war between the forces of right and wrong—merciless warfare—war without quarter.

CHAPTER XVIII

Dan Is Shrewd

THE two reporter-detectives banged the Clarion office door behind them and climbed into Leslie Wysong's small roadster. Dan started the motor and they pulled away from the curb. A half block away, Corbin Watson watched them go with spying eyes.

Dan and Billy had the car at their command. Leslie had offered it to them. "Don't worry about me," she had said. "And don't worry about the Clarion."

Few people were on the streets as Dan deftly swung their borrowed "chariot" into Main Street. It was still quite early and they had not breakfasted.

"How about something to eat?"

"Sure, Dan. We can at least start things right —on full stomachs. Let's have our java and rolls. I'm beginning to feel a void in my tummy. Time, tide, and the tummy ache wait for no man, you know, so let's eat."

"Ptomaine Joe's place isn't open. We'll eat at the station lunch wagon. Then we'll really begin operations, before this town is full of police and big town reporters. It won't take long for them to sense a big story and come rushing down here."

Dan applied the brakes and they skidded to a fast stop before the lunch cart. Inside all was noisy confusion. The Chicago and Southern freight and yard crews were discussing the happenings of the early morning with loud excitement. Nothing like the Midnight Special mystery had ever taken place before on any railroad. The veterans were quite sure of that. Dan and Billy found it impossible to converse in the din.

"Let's run out to the scene of the big disappearance," Dan suggested when they had finished eating and were once more in the car. "We're not going to get anywhere by sticking around Norfolk."

The street scene had become more active, even in the short time they had spent at breakfast. There was excitement in the crisp morning air. Men gathered in little knots on street corners and a crowd had formed around the station, where the agent was detailing the latest developments to interested hearers.

"The ol' burg is waking up," Dan observed. "The good citizens are discovering that something happened during their hours of peaceful slumber."

Dan stopped the car again before the station. "Better run in and catch up on the new developments," he suggested. "We don't want to overlook anything important, you know. Les will cover the story for the Clarion, but I want to know the whole tale, for my own information."

"Yes," Billy assented. "That's a swell idea. We might be able to draw a few conclusions."

"Well, hustle in there. I'll wait. I don't think I'll park the car. It takes too long."

Billy was gone only a short while; he returned to the car grinning from ear to ear and vigorously shaking his head, obviously amused. When they were again on their way down Main Street, now alive with people, he explained.

"The station agent makes me laugh," he said. "He's running around like a chicken with its head cut off. From his actions, you'd gather that Vance Murray was holding him directly responsible for all that has taken place."

"Myers is a pompous little nobody," Dan swung Leslie Wysong's automobile onto High Street. They were headed for the open country, and only a few blocks separated them from the beginning of the state road. The roadster rolled briskly along the shaded street with sure speed.

"Learn anything new?" Dan went on.

"Yes."

"Spill it."

"Vance Murray and a corps of private detectives will arrive by special train this afternoon, and the governor has already assigned the expert operatives of the state police to the case. They are to arrive from Indianapolis this noon, if the missing train doesn't turn up in the meantime."

"No one has been successful in trailing the Special then?"

"Of course not, Dan. When that bandit-manned choo-choo pulled away from Tower XY, it vanished into thin air. No one has the slightest idea as to what became of it. The mail is gone. So is the Chicago and Southern pay roll money. Lucian Kyle's fancy protective invention went with the cars. The smart lads behind the robbery were bright enough to prevent detection by stealing the entire train!"

Dan sighed. "We're up against a tough proposition, and we must work absolutely on our own. I'm glad we're getting an early start."

Billy agreed with him. "The whole thing is fantastic—too crazy to be true, but true it is." His face lighted suddenly with an idea. "Say, perhaps the Special has been hidden on some siding between here and Louisville. That's a possibility."

"You mean it *was*," corrected his friend. "Only two trains have gone through this morning and one has come from the other way. None of them saw anything of the missing Special, and the section crews have checked all the sidings leading away from the railroad. There isn't a trace of the train. We might as well recognize that fact."

They left Norfolk behind and roared down the concrete of the state road toward where the blue of the sky blended with the white of pavement among low hills. Wooded land stretched away from them.

"We leave this highway in a few minutes," Dan announced. "The rest of the trip will be over back roads, and they won't be any too smooth. You may count on that."

"This is swell—riding along like we are," Billy laughed. The wind was blowing his hair. His eyes were bright and he was ready for adventure—anything.

"Wait till we hit a side road," Dan warned. "You may change your tune."

"Maybe, pal. But I don't think I shall."

The time came soon enough for Billy to "eat" his too optimistic words. When Dan and Billy finally did turn from the main highway, they exchanged concrete for loose, heavy gravel. The roadway curved above a deep ravine. Sunlight fought its way through green leaves. They enjoyed the musical song of a bubbling spring as it sparkled amongst moss covered rocks and then flowed more gently to become a narrow silvery creek.

"Quite a morning," Dan exclaimed.

Billy nodded and smiled. He was enjoying to the utmost the lovely brilliance of the sunshine.

Billy suddenly gripped the side of the roadster. They jolted over large stones and tipped alarmingly as the eccentric road twisted and slanted toward the rocky ravine.

"This *is* a road!" Dan laughed.

"A road?" Billy queried. "Do you call this atrocity a road?"

A long torturous drive over three equally poor back roads finally brought them to the Chicago and Southern tracks in the vicinity of Tower XY. Here the railroad curved through low undulating hills; here the single track of the main line shimmered in the brightness of the morning, and a deceptive calm hung along the steeply banked right of way.

"We have arrived," announced Dan, stopping the car and pulling at the hand brake, all in one motion. "We've driven as far as we can. The rest of the journey will be made on foot."

"How far do we walk?" asked Billy Parker.

"About a quarter of a mile. We'll amble along the ties."

They piled out of the car and climbed carefully over an old fashioned rail fence, crossed a small ditch, and were on railroad property.

"I think we hike north." Dan was not very sure. "The hotel clerk told me how to find the tower, and I think I left the car at the right spot. If I did, we go up the track—not down toward Norfolk."

"I, for one, hope a train doesn't come breezing along and bump us while we're tramping between the rails," said Billy. "I don't want the back of my lap made all black and blue."

"We'll listen for trains," Dan answered.

"You bet we will. I'm going to put my ear against one of the rails every so often. Little Billy is taking no chances."

They walked along the ties in silence. Only the sharp song of the wind in the telegraph wires strung beside the tracks broke the stillness. They breathed cool, pure air.

Dan picked up a stone and sent it sailing. The missile struck its mark, one of the telegraph poles, with a loud thump. The sharpshooter grinned in triumph.

"All right, you're good," Billy admitted, "but we're not making very fast progress. Come on, get a move on."

A curve in the track five hundred yards farther on brought Tower XY and the railroad cross-over into view. The tower, standing against the paleness of the sky on its long stilt-like legs, seemed only a short distance away. A little knot of men stood near the cross-over. The roughly dressed members of a Chicago and Southern section crew patrolled the right of way. They seemed to be carefully searching in the long grass bordering the gravel and steel rails.

"Here we are," announced Dan. "We didn't have far to come after all, Billy."

As they neared the crowd of men about the tower, one of the group walked down the tracks toward them. He was a big, heavy man dressed in a windbreaker and a battered felt hat.

"Aha," Dan observed, "our approach has been noted and an official 'greeter' has been sent ahead to welcome us." Then in a much more serious tone he said, "I wonder what this guy wants, Billy?"

"Don't ask me. I'm merely a stranger from the big city."

"I hope he's friendly. I brought my police

press pass along. The railroad people may honor it and let us poke around and do some sleuthing and then again they may not. We'll soon know."

The man in the bulky windbreaker shouted to them in a demanding voice when he was a few hundred feet away.

"What are you two doing here?" The tone was harsh, as rough as its owner.

Dan and Billy were standing between the rails. "He doesn't sound very pleasant," the young editor observed quite correctly. "And he certainly does not look pleasant. Well, all he can do is tell us to get off railroad property. I know our rights. This fellow is a railroad detective."

"I'm glad you do, because I'm in the dark on reporters' privileges. I didn't even know we had any."

Billy Parker regarded the approaching Chicago and Southern railroad policeman with wary eyes that also measured the distance between himself and the fence.

CHAPTER XIX

The Stone Wall

DAN brought forth his most disarming smile and turned its full force on the gruff railroad detective standing between the rails with his feet spread far apart. It was do or die now, and the young editor wanted permission to carefully inspect the ground around the signal tower.

"You guys will have to get out of here," the officious detective yelled at them. "This is railroad property and we don't want no company. You can't stay on railroad property without a pass. That's the law."

"We *have* passes," Dan countered brightly.

"Let's see 'em," was the demand.

Dan promptly handed over the press pass which the Norfolk and state police had issued to him. Billy surrendered his Chicago Star pass.

The detective handed back the cards and waved them on. "O.k. Look around all you want, but don't get in our hair." He was evidently satisfied with their credentials.

"The well trained newshawk is never in the way," Billy informed him.

Dan and Billy went on down the tracks toward Tower XY, leaving the arm of the law still standing open mouthed beside the rails. They whistled a gay tune; they were at last on the scene, ready for action.

"Now, we get down to business, eh?"

"Righto, Billy."

"—And what's first on the program? Do we talk to these birds gathered around the tower?"

"We do. Perhaps they've made a few discoveries, but I'm afraid that is too much to hope for."

They joined the group at the tower's base and once more were asked to show their credentials. When the formality had been dispensed with, they carefully looked about them and asked questions.

Dan shook his head sadly as he and Billy left the others ten minutes later. "I was afraid we wouldn't learn anything new from the railroad police. They either haven't come upon any important clues, or else they're being darned close mouthed."

"I'm inclined to believe in the first conclusion," Billy said. "I think the private bluecoats here are baffled. I *know* I am. How about yourself?"

"I'm in the same boat, fellow."

"Well, they say misery loves company. So far, we have only drawn blanks in our own little hunt for the missing train. Anyway, at least we know how it was abducted. We know that it went over the cross-over and puffed off into the dark, and we know that Slauson, the previously kidnapped engineer, was more than likely its unwilling pilot."

They took in their surroundings once again, hoping to see something which might point a kindly guiding finger toward a logical explanation of the mystery. Everything was as usual. Fertile fields, wooded land, and gently rolling hills surrounded the Tower XY junction. Telegraph poles stood evenly spaced along the Chicago and Southern right of way, gaunt, mute witnesses to the greatest railroad mystery of the decade. Where had the train gone? Where was it now? How had the ghost gang been able to make it leave the rails and completely vanish into thin air? The perplexing questions pounded into Dan's brain. He must somehow, somewhere find the answers to those questions—and soon. He must not fail. He must not. The goading words dinned in his ears. Failure—ruin. They meant the same—were synonymous. And to Dan's harassed mind came the troubling thought that the ghost gang might strike again—might steal yet another treasure laden train!

Billy broke in on his thoughts. "Do you suppose the Special passed through Norfolk?"

Dan shook his head sadly. "No, they watched for it from five o'clock on. It couldn't possibly have gone through before that time. When a train moves, it makes a noise."

"All right. Then the Special must have disappeared somewhere between here and the Norfolk station."

"You're right, but we've gone over that point before."

"Sure, but not in this way. We can narrow down the miles of track more than likely traversed by the missing engine and cars by checking back along the line to Norfolk."

"I'm beginning to get you, lad. Trains make noise, lots of it, and the engines which pull them are equipped with big headlights."

"But suppose all of the lights were turned off and the glow from the firebox masked? What then?"

"We still have the noise to go by. You can't run a train without making a racket. It's an impossibility. Someone near the railroad surely must have heard the kidnapped Special after it left the XY junction. Perhaps we can trace it accurately enough to discover approximately the place where it was last heard or seen. Then we'll scour the neighboring countryside, and perhaps —perhaps, I say—we may find our engine and cars and solve our mystery."

"You make everything sound easy, Dan."

"Do I? Well, it won't be easy—tracking down the missing Midnight Special. We'll practically have to stalk it on our hands and knees."

They laughed and quickly felt better. Although their visit to the junction signal tower had revealed no new clues, it had at least suggested a good plan of action.

"Before we leave, let's have a look at the lay of the land," Billy suggested. "I want to have a look at the country from the top of the signal tower. Then we'll stalk our train."

From the tower they could see the two railroad lines cross at right angles. No switches or sidings connected the two tracks.

They climbed down out of the tower and went back along the rails to where they had left Leslie's car.

"Too bad this jitney isn't equipped with flanged wheels," Billy commented. "We could run it along the track and save our poor feet many weary miles."

"Wishing isn't going to take us very far," Dan reminded him, "but I think we can manage a ride. We can if you're willing to work for it."

"Explain yourself."

"Two of the railroad detectives are planning to pump their way into Norfolk on a hand car. I heard them talking a minute ago. They've borrowed a car assigned to the section gang which makes Tower XY its headquarters. We'll leave Leslie's roadster here and send back for it later on. We'll flag the policemen when they come through."

"Suppose they don't want our company?"

"I think they will. They'll be good and tired of pumping that hand driven go-cart along the rails. Two extra pumpers will more than likely be greatly appreciated."

"I hope you're right."

Dan was sure of himself. "Wait and see."

They had not long to wait for the muscle propelled taxi. Puffing and panting from the exertion of running the car, the two railroad policemen were glad of the chance to have extra hands grasp the long handlebars. Dan and Billy stepped aboard and began to pump. The four made the little car shoot down the tracks with unusual speed.

"Even the Special would have a hard time catching up with us now," Dan laughed as they shot around a steeply banked curve. The handle-bars flew up and down like a teeter-totter suddenly gone mad. A strong breeze brushed cooling, tender fingers across his hot face.

The day passed with magic swiftness. Almost before Dan and Billy knew it, lunchtime had come and gone. They had crackers and bread and cool, refreshing milk at a country store near the Chicago and Southern railroad right of way.

There were but three tiny villages between Tower XY and Norfolk. The railroad did not maintain stations at any of the trio, providing only cinder platforms and faded signs giving the name of each village. When they reached the first, Ridgedale, Dan and Billy jumped from the handcar, ready to ask questions, and the railroad policemen kept on toward Norfolk. Ridgedale proved to be a general store and four scattered and dingy frame bungalows.

"A local accommodation train stops here in about a half hour," Dan said. "We'll hop it and ride into the next village, Skunk Valley. It's another three or four miles down the line."

"Well, we're in Ridgedale now, Dan. Let's question the natives. If the Special went through here last night, someone must have heard it."

The Midnight Special had roared through Ridgedale!

It took them only ten minutes to discover that four people in Ridgedale had actually seen the missing Special *pass through the village!* Others had heard it. No one had noticed anything unusual about the train at the time, but Dan's questions brought out several interesting facts which the two young men filed away in their active minds for future reference:

The Midnight Special had passed through Ridgedale with the usual lights burning on the engine, in the cars, and on the end of the observation car.

The train had roared through at a speed greater than usual. Its bell was operating and it had whistled for grade crossings in the regular manner.

"Now we're getting places," Dan exclaimed when they were back on the cinder platform which served the tiny place as a railroad station. "We know the train came through here, and we've received the information before anyone else. In another half hour or so the state and railroad detectives will swarm in here and ask practically the same questions. We're a jump ahead of them."

"When's the local due?"

"In about five minutes. We won't have to hang around here long. I'm as anxious as you are to get on to Skunk Valley."

Billy left the platform and kneeled between the rails, resting his head on the steel.

"Hear anything?" Dan queried.

"Nope. Can't hear a thing."

"Perhaps the train's coming on tip-toe," he was told, "or then again it may be wearing carpet slippers or rubbers. It may be quietly stalking a cow, just as we're tracking one of its brother trains."

Ten minutes later the lazy accommodation came wandering along and the two young men climbed aboard the single coach. Three railroad detectives got off as Dan and Billy found a seat. The shabby little local coughed away from the cinder platform which was the Ridgedale station.

"There—what did I tell you!" Dan crowed. "We're a jump ahead of the authorities, and we're going to stay one leap ahead."

Skunk Valley proved to be an uninviting collection of rough shacks. It could not even boast of a general store, and when Dan and Billy stepped from the train, there seemed to be nothing around but valley, the huts of the village, bleak prairie, a dozen scrawny chickens, and a few empty milk cans.

The Special had been heard but not seen in Skunk Valley! Almost the entire population had heard the Special thunder through shortly before dawn. It was now obvious to Dan and Billy that the train had vanished somewhere between Skunk Valley and Norfolk.

Two aged citizens of the town had seen the Special's headlight. Both also had heard the thunder of the train. "She always make a big racket when she highballs into the valley," one of their informers had said. "She was right on time this morning."

Their mission in Skunk Valley accomplished, Dan announced that the next stop would be Savanna, the last of the three small villages between Tower XY and Norfolk. The only other hamlet in the vicinity was Kiowa, a mile away from the tracks on the highway. They would stop at Kiowa later on. Savanna was their immediate concern, and they were forced to cover the distance on foot.

During the two mile walk to the last of the three villages, both young men had a fine chance to discuss with each other their theories concerning the disappearance of the Midnight Special. Dan told his friend about the two kidnappings of the railroad men and of Con Sheldon. "I'm certain Sheldon is connected in some way with all of the crimes," he said surely. "The tires on a car owned by a friend of Sheldon's, a man named Edwards, make imprints identical with the tire marks I obtained from the scene of the first kidnapping. I've seen Sheldon driving Edwards' car around Norfolk. He probably borrowed it for that one evening. The local officials have never made any great effort to solve either kidnapping. Both victims were practically alone in the world, so there were no families to worry about the abductions and keep after the authorities."

Billy was inclined to agree with his friend's deductions, and he said so. "If you can capture the ghost gang and send Sheldon to the 'big house,' you're made here in Indiana," he told Dan.

"I know that," the other replied. "That's why I'm so anxious for success."

As they walked, aeroplanes droned overhead, circling, zooming, and diving—trim ships which were obviously searching for the lost train.

"I wonder if they'll locate it?" Billy said,

shading his eyes from the sun and peering up into the smooth, soft blue of the sky. "I sorta hope they don't. I want us to be the ones to come across that train."

Dan laughed, a little sheepishly. "I just had the same thought myself."

"Do you think they really will find the Special from the clouds?"

"No I don't. The lads who stole Vance Murray's speedy pet flyer are clever. They were bright enough to make the engines and cars disappear into thin air, so they have more than likely either done away with the train altogether in some miraculous manner, or have found a good hiding place for it."

The pair trudged on and stepped away from the tracks as the special train bearing Vance Murray to Norfolk thundered by.

"We won't recognize the old town when we get back from this little excursion," Dan observed. "It'll be like Atlantic City at a convention time and far more excited. I'm glad we both have our own rooms at the hotel."

"We'd better get back to town as soon as we can," Billy was getting a little anxious. "I've got to telephone the Star. Gargan will boil me in oil if I let anything of importance connected with the Midnight Special mystery slip through my fingers. I want to let the boys on the city desk in on all the latest developments. We'll scoop every other daily paper in the country."

"We'll go back to Norfolk as soon as we're finished at Savanna. You can take care of your business while I talk things over with Leslie Wysong. Then I'll hire an auto from Alf Good-hue and we'll go out to the tower and get her car."

They walked into the last village a few minutes later on, quite weary and footsore. Savanna was like its predecessors—a tiny collection of shabby, nondescript buildings ranged along one wide muddy street.

At the lone store they learned that the Midnight Special *had not* gone through Savanna! No one in the tiny town had seen or heard the train that morning. Each and every villager was sure it had not passed.

"I generally hear 'er shoot through," the store-keeper told Dan. "I don't sleep well, so I hear 'er whistle and clatter by regular. She didn't show up this mornin'. I'll swear tuh that."

All the other Savanna citizens interviewed were equally as positive of the one important fact: the Special had not passed through Savanna. Somewhere between Skunk Valley and Savanna—somewhere along the very section of track which Dan and Billy had themselves traversed—somewhere in the early morning darkness the Midnight Special had vanished into nowhere.

Billy Parker came into the Clarion office fairly bursting with news and information. He scorned the little gate leading into what Dan liked to call his private office and leaped over the low railing.

"Why the hurry?" Dan looked up from the still damp galley proof of Leslie Wysong's story and editorial announcing the Clarion's intention of finding the Special.

"Oh, I'm just excited. The town's filled with railroad dicks and newspaper men. All our old pals are here. You'd think there was a political convention or a three ring circus going on, and the telegraph office looks like the city press bureau."

"That means we must work fast. What did you find out about the aeroplanes—the ones we saw flying above us? Did they dig up anything?"

"Absolutely nothing, Dan. They flew over the very spot where the train must have disappeared and they couldn't find a trace of the Special."

Dan was perplexed and an expression of bafflement had taken possession of his pleasant face.

He sighed. "This is a swell state of affairs. We walked that stretch of track ourselves and we didn't notice anything the least bit unusual during our hike. The train must have left the main line between Skunk Valley and Savanna, yet we saw no trace of it, and there were no switches or sidings—nothing in the least bit suspicious. Well, we'll have to go over the same ground more carefully tonight or tomorrow. If we find nothing then—well, we're up against a stone wall. A stone wall difficult to surmount."

CHAPTER XX

The Wall Crumbles

DAN'S "stone wall" prediction material-
ized late that same afternoon. Dan sent
Biff Little, the printer's devil, after
Leslie's car and prepared for more action. The
girl had issued a challenging extra edition of the
Clarion and had the office routine under ad-
mirable control. Dan and Billy were free to
pursue their detective work after Billy had informed the Star by telephone of the latest developments. The city was alive with out of town
reporters, railroad men, and detectives.

Anxious to thoroughly explore the territory
along the C and S tracks between Skunk Valley
and Savanna, Dan hired two big touring cars
and enlisted the services of eight Norfolk Boy
Scouts. All of them were Clarion delivery boys
as well as Scouts, and Dan knew that he could
depend upon his youthful aides. Glad to do a
"good turn" for Dan, all of the boys were eagerly
interested in the adventure before them. The
party left Norfolk in the early evening armed
with guns, flashlamps, and stout sticks.

They stopped at the hamlet of Kiowa on the way to interview the storekeeper there. Billy went in and returned shaking his head.

"They couldn't tell me much," he explained. "Kiowa is too far from the tracks and the C and S trains are seldom heard here. But the storekeeper claims that he heard an explosion just before dawn, and the noise seemed to come from the north."

"He probably mistook thunder for an explosion," Dan decided, "and even an explosion in that direction could have little or nothing to do with the missing train. It was last heard at Skunk Valley—which is more east than north of Kiowa. Did the storekeeper think that the sound of the explosion came from the north?"

"Yes, Dan, he told me that it seemed to come from that direction. But the train was reported at Skunk Valley, east of Kiowa."

"Well, I guess the noise didn't have anything to do with the disappearance of the train. Then again, what the storekeeper thought was an explosion might have been something else."

"What for instance?" Billy was being persistent.

"Oh, thunder."

"Last night was clear," Billy reminded him quietly.

They left the cars near Skunk Valley and once more hiked along the railroad. During the waning hours of the day they carefully searched the right of way between Skunk Valley and Savanna, looking for some little thing—some tiny clue which might lead them to the missing train. And they were not alone. Railway police patrolled the right of way, tramped over the hilly land beside the track. The Chicago and Southern railroad detectives and the state troopers had also decided that the Midnight Special had disappeared somewhere on that particular stretch of track. Had not the train been heard in Skunk Valley? Had not its whistle sounded there? Had not a glaring headlight pierced the night as the Special roared through the valley—never to appear at Savanna?

The determined search of Dan and Billy and their assisting Boy Scouts was in vain. So were the painstaking efforts of the state police and the railroad detectives. Men swarmed along the right of way; determined plain clothes men penetrated far into the wooded hills, their flashlamps winking and swinging in the brooding darkness.

Failure.

The Midnight Special had been missing for fifteen hours now.

Failure.

"We've got to do something," Dan groaned. "Why, we're already beginning to take the railroad's place as the laughing stock of the town—and the county as well. We've got to make good the Clarion's promise to find the train and round up the ghost gang in a hurry."

"You're telling me!" Leslie Wysong, sprawled, completely worn out, in her office chair, spoke grimly. "I saw Con Sheldon on the street this afternoon, and he had evidently read my editorial and news story in today's extra. He was wearing a smile which was almost a plain out and out sneer, and he said: 'Your boss is a big wind bag. He'll never find that train. Tell him to get out of town before I have him run out.'"

"That settles it," Dan declared, pounding with his fist on the desk before him. "Sheldon's mixed up in those train robberies. We've got to prove he is—and do it before he has a chance to harm me or the paper. We must keep the confidence of the people too—by solving the mystery."

"Well then, what's the next move, General?" Billy Parker stood near the Clarion office door. "As for me, I'm tired and darned discouraged."

"So are the rest of us," Dan reminded him. "Let's all get out of here and have a good night's sleep."

"Great idea!" Billy agreed. "I'm ready to turn in. There's nothing else to do tonight, unless something important turns up."

"Police headquarters will call the hotel in that event," Dan told him. "Let's go."

They left the room for the late evening darkness of the street, and Leslie Wysong stepped into her roadster, which had been brought back to the office.

"Can I give you two a ride to the Norfolk House?"

"No thanks, Les. We'll walk. It's not far and the air will do us both good."

"You're right, it will, though you've had plenty of it today. Good night. See you in the morning, and remember—when you come upon a stone wall, climb over or, better still, go around."

"Thanks loads for the bedtime advice, Les. You've been a brick—perfectly swell."

"Don't flatter me, Dan. I just want to do my part. I'll run the Clarion while you and Billy detect."

"You're doing a better job than we are," he declared.

She started the roadster, and its noisy voice shattered the stillness. Dan and Billy began to walk slowly away from the Clarion building as

the twin tail lights of the car flickered in the growing distance.

"Great gal—Les," Dan praised.

"Sure, a swell sport," Billy added.

They went on in silence, each busy with his
thoughts and passed into the pale circle of light
cast by the street lamp at the mouth of the alley
running behind the Clarion office. Suddenly Dan
grabbed his friend's arm and jerked him back
into the shadows.

"What's the big idea?" Billy started to ask,
but Dan clapped a none too gentle hand over
his mouth and pointed down the alley to the
spot where it passed the dark hulk of the Clarion
building. A man was running along the alley—
away from the building.

"Come on, Billy! After him!" Dan whispered
hoarsely. The two newspaper men slipped noise-
lessly down the alley, keeping to the shadows.
The man before them made no effort to conceal
his haste. Sensing that he was being followed, he
hurried along the pavement. His young pur-
surers gained on him rapidly. Realizing that he
could not outdistance the pair, he stopped suddenly and whipped around to face them. Dan
and Billy were fifty feet away.

"Stay where you are! I've got a gun." The
voice was calm and yet savage. The face they

saw was that of a man at bay, a man cornered and desperate. The words were snarled at them.

"He's got a gun. Watch out!" cried Dan as Billy darted for the protective corner of the building.

Their enemy turned so that the rays from the light at the mouth of the alley fell upon his flushed face, and Dan made a startling discovery.

"It's Watson—one of Con Sheldon's henchmen!" he cried. "Come on, we've got to capture him."

Dan leaped recklessly forward and made a valiant flying dive for the legs of Corbin Watson. Then suddenly livid red flame spat in the darkness and three bullets shrilled past Dan and bit harmlessly into the wall of a garage. Watson ducked and Dan hit the alley pavement with a jarring thud. Billy came out from behind the garage, a heavy brick in each hand. Billy took careful aim and hurled both bricks. Corbin Watson saw him just in time and ducked, but not quite soon enough. The second brick crashed into his shoulder. He shrilly cried out in pain, and turned and ran down the alley. Billy started after him as Dan struggled to his feet. They pounded along together over the rather uneven paving.

Out of the alley they rushed and over vacant

lots. Weeds and briars tore at their clothes, ripped their trouser legs, but they kept on. They turned into a better lighted street, about three hundred feet apart, and the two young men suddenly realized what their quarry was planning. He was heading for the railroad yards and, once there, he would be safe from pursuit. They lengthened their strides, but still could not overtake Watson. Two more blocks were covered and then he escaped into the safety of the long lines of freight cars. Lights gleamed from the searchlights suspended on masts above the maze of tracks but the lanes between the cars were in complete darkness. They had lost their man.

"We might as well go back to the hotel," Dan panted. "He's safe now, and I don't want to flirt with death around the freight cars."

Tired, bruised, and angry with themselves, they slowly made their way back to the street. Dan hailed a cruising taxicab and they were driven to the Norfolk House.

In the hotel they separated, each getting his key at the desk and going to his own room.

As Dan put his key into the door he was disturbed by a noise coming from his own room; he was sure it was the sound of a window being slowly opened. Someone must be entering his room. It would be simple for an intruder to climb the fire escape and then transfer to the narrow balcony outside his windows.

A street car a block away clanged for an intersection, but as the sound died away Dan again heard the noise that had aroused his attention. It was muffled—plainly coming through the door. He was sure now! Someone was in his room.

Dan turned the doorknob, opening his door a fraction of an inch at a time. He could discern the shadowy figure of a man bending over the desk near his bed. The window behind the desk let in just enough light to silhouette the intruder.

Dan had one foot in the room when the door creaked noisily, giving him away. The finger of light which had been upon the desk shot up and struck him full in the face. Dan uttered an involuntary cry and leaped forward with reckless courage. A heavy paperweight whistled through the air—just missing his head and crashed against the door. A command followed it.

"Stay where you are—you fool! I've got a gun!"

Dan moved forward.

The command snapped through the dark room a second time. "Stay where you are!"

Dan jumped toward the voice and was almost on the invader when he caught the gleam of an automatic. Flame flashed, stabbing toward Dan, and a rocking report reverberated through the room. The bullet shrilled past his head and spat into the wall. He flung out his fists. Before the other could fire again, Dan was on him, grappling at close quarters for the gun. They tumbled to the floor and rolled over and over, first one on top and then the other. They crashed into the desk and the intruder cried out in sudden pain. The gun skidded along the floor and the desperate fight was resumed.

They regained their feet. Dan smashed home a fast blow which caught the other on the chin. There was a crack and the invader slumped to the floor. Dan stood over him, panting.

He picked up the tiny flashlight the intruder had been using and turned its rays downward. A huddled form lay on the floor—white face streaked with blood, eyes closed. . . . Then suddenly he was in the midst of another battle.

He whirled at the first sound. Black figures had leaped into the room from the window— three men. Two sprang upon him, gripping their automatics by the barrels. The other went to the man on the floor.

Dan struck out swiftly, with telling blows, as the pair rushed him. A gun butt slashed hard against his temple. A second knocked viciously against the side of his head. Brutal, savage, merciless, the onslaught was more than any man could battle. Sheldon had made no idle threat.

Dancing lights spun in Dan's aching head and became a roaring pinwheel as he dropped to the floor.

When Dan awoke he was stretched on his own bed and Billy Parker was bending over him. His head ached but he was ready for action. Aside from Billy, the room was empty.

"They got away," Bill said. "When I heard the noise and came in to investigate they were on their way down the fire escape. I called the police, but my alarm didn't do any good."

Dan climbed out of bed and washed his face in the bathroom. Then he drank some water and felt better. There was a big bruise on his forehead and another on his cheek.

He came back into the bedroom and flopped into a chair. "No hits—no runs—lots of errors," he commented pessimistically. "What a day!"

Dan stood by the window and opened it wide to admit the fragrance of the night. A cool, caressing breeze brushed over his hot face and body, bringing infinite relief from the worry and pain which racked his troubled mind.

For a full five minutes he stood on the tiny balcony outside his window—alone with the fresh night.

"Coming to bed, Dan?" Billy asked.

"In a minute." The words were muffled.

"Well, I'm going back to my room. S'long. They won't come back."

There was no answer. Billy Parker smiled, shrugged his shoulders, and heaved himself out of the chair. He left the room, carefully closing the door behind him.

In the street below the little balcony a raucous advertising truck equipped with loud speakers and a public address system was shouting the merits of Superba Soup and playing scratchy phonograph records. The noise penetrated into the consciousness of the young editor. He stared down at the truck—then the expression on his face changed with startling suddenness from annoyance to amazed understanding. Turning, he rapidly climbed back through the window. Gone was the peace of the previous moment.

"Billy! Come here—quick!" Dan's voice crackled with great excitement.

Frightened, Billy Parker bounced in from the next room, throwing his dressing gown around his shoulders as he came.

"What's up?"

"Plenty, Billy. Plenty. Get your shirt and coat on. Hurry!"

"Why—may I ask?"

"You and I are leaving the hotel right away, and we're going to be gone all night."

"Have you gone mad?" Billy stared at him, mouth open.

"No, I'm not crazy. In fact, I'm unusually sane—for the first time since the train disappeared. I've been a blind fool, Billy. A blind fool! But now I'm beginning to see the light. I know where the ghost gang is hiding the Midnight Special."

CHAPTER XXI

The Truth Arrives

DAN dragged Billy Parker out of the hotel and into Alf Goodhue's taxicab. When the machine jerked forward and they were on their way to the Clarion office, he began to explain.

"I can see everything now," Dan crowed in triumph. "At the present moment, I'm playing a strong hunch. Everything we've learned today about the missing flyer indicates that I'm right.

"The train passed through Ridgedale—was positively identified there. Then it proceeded on South, and the good people of Skunk Valley claim that they heard it and saw its headlight. But it didn't show up at Savanna, the third station. That fact has concentrated almost the entire search, official and otherwise, on the stretch of C. and S. track between Skunk Valley and Savanna. The train has not been found. But I know where it is hiding, and I'm going to prove that the missing Midnight Special *never went through Skunk Valley!*"

"Whew!" Billy whistled. "And what brought you to that amazing conclusion?"

"That's partly a secret, but I'll say this much: Remember the storekeeper at Kiowa? He told you he heard an explosion to the north. Well, I think he did. Kiowa is on an east-west line with Skunk Valley. An explosion in that direction fits into our picture *if* we decide that the Special never reached Skunk Valley. My own eyes were opened when I happened to glance down into the street from my hotel window. I saw something there that set my mind to working."

"I hope your hunch is O.K., Dan. We're certainly going into action tonight." Billy was eager and curious. The cab came to a stop.

At the Clarion office Dan eagerly searched through file after file of old issues of the paper. He finally found the edition for which he had been searching, and, after reading for a moment, he put it down and once more rushed Billy into the street.

"Why did you hunt up that piece in the paper, Dan? What has it got to do with our mystery?"

"Plenty," Dan barked. They were on their way to the Chicago and Southern freight yards, again in Alf Goodhue's cab. "When I first came to Norfolk, I went through all the Clarion files and in one of the issues I read about an old abandoned quarry located nearly two miles from the Chicago and Southern tracks and west and south of Ridgedale. I wanted to refresh my memory on that story. That's why we stopped at the office."

"But why are we headed for the freight yards?"

"Because there's a fast freight due to leave for La Fayette in about five minutes. We're going to ride that freight as far as Ridgedale and do some fancy investigating."

Thrilled by the adventure which the night had brought them, they dismissed Goodhue and his taxi and walked into the gloom of the freight yards. Their feet crunched softly in the cinders. They pushed cautiously ahead into the blackness. Trouble might lurk in the frightening shadows.

A mournful whistle shrieked, breaking a heavy silence. Then they heard the panting of a freight engine. "They're hooking the freight engine onto the head of the train," Dan explained. "We'd better climb aboard one of the box cars."

The pair trudged around long strings of empties and gondolas and finally came to the starting track. A great engine was already jerking its long train forward. The pair grabbed for the iron rungs at the end of a box car and climbed to the roof. As the train gained speed and clacked

over the yard switches, they settled themselves
and prepared for a chilly, dirty ride. Smoke and
cinders from the hard working engine billowed
and swirled about them, making them miserable.

"Look! Look ahead!" Dan suddenly pointed
an excited finger down the long line of swaying
car tops.

"It's Watson," Billy yelled above the savage
roar of the train. They could make out the features of the other man as the last of the yard
lights illuminated him.

"Duck—quick, before he sees us!" Dan
ordered. They crawled along to the end of the car
and then climbed part way down the brake
ladder between the cars. The heavy exhaust of
the engine barked in the night as it cleared the
yard limit interlock tower. Clear board ahead!
Green lanterns waved and bobbed beside the
right of way.

The fast freight whipped around a curve and
Norfolk was now only a nest of twinkling lights
behind them. Dan and Billy climbed back to the
top of the car as the yard lights faded and the
locomotive picked up speed for its run to
LaFayette. Somewhere ahead of them in the
darkness was Corbin Watson. Dan and Billy
crept slowly forward, clutching the runway with
their hands—intent on finding his hiding place.

While the freight thundered toward Savanna, they made slow and exceptionally difficult progress over the tops of the swaying cars. Once, when the firebox opened and painted the dark a flaming crimson, Billy thought he saw a shadowy form three or four car lengths ahead. Watson had more than likely taken refuge in one of the gondolas at the head of the train. There were about ten cars between them and the engine, so they were sure that they would be able to spot their quarry if he left the train.

The freight lurched its way into timbered valley and the moon struggled through the clouds. They were speeding into wooded country and farm land. Occasionally flickering lights could be seen along the right of way. Railroad detectives and state troopers were still searching for tiny clues which might lead to the discovery of the Midnight Special—and were finding none. The train flashed through a village. Dark houses were huddled close to the mothering railroad; a light glimmered in a closed store. That would be Savanna. Dan and Billy continued to creep slowly forward along the top of the cars.

They waited until the train was nearing Skunk Valley before they attempted to shift themselves from the last box car in the train to the first of the gondolas. The change meant a dangerous leap to the bucking platform on the end of the gondola, but they jumped recklessly, flying through the dark, and gripped the steel brake rod set into the end of the platform to steady themselves. They sprawled upon the little platform, regained their balance, and hung on. The night was beginning to be more than chilly, and the speed of the train intensified their discomfort. They had no great desire to meet up with Watson at that moment, preferring a battle on the ground to a hand to hand fight above the speeding wheels of a fast freight.

The moon went under the clouds and the night once more became heavy and dark. The biting chill in the air increased and they beat their hands together to keep them warm. A few feeble lights gleamed as they shot over a short bridge. They swung around a sweeping curve, and roared up a short grade, the staccato bark of the stack a powerful song in the night.

The train jerked and bucked as the engineer opened his throttle wide for the steeply graded climb to Skunk Valley and the speed increased until the clickety-clack of the wheels on the rail joints merged into a loud blur of uneven sound. The cars wheeled around curves at an almost dizzy speed and both Dan and Billy were forced to hold on to the hand irons with all their strength to keep from being flung from the train. Then the speed slackened again as they struck the actual grade and the roll and pitch of the train lessened somewhat.

The freight topped the grade at Skunk Valley and eased down the other side. The tiny village swept past, a hodge-podge of strange shadows. The roar of the locomotive's exhaust was now reduced to a low throaty rumble, so both young men knew that they were drifting down the short grade toward Canadian Creek and the water tanks used by the Chicago and Southern freight engines. The train shuddered as a heavy reduction on the air line clamped brake shoes against spinning wheels. They rumbled over the creek bridge, and Dan took a firm grip on the hand irons and leaned far out from the side of the gondola. Ahead, the beam of the engine's headlight knifed the dark with a brilliant swath of light. He made out the fat twin water tanks, huddled together.

"We mustn't lose our man," Billy reminded Dan as he swung out.

Dan nodded. "We won't. He may leave the train here, and if he does, we follow him. He may lead us to the Midnight Special."

"I thought you were going direct to the quarry?"

"Finding Watson on this train changes things. I want to grab the ghost gang, remember. If my hunch is good, Watson will more than likely take us to the quarry. He's our game right now, and we're not going to let him get away from us."

"I'll be glad of the chance to stretch my legs without risking my life at the same time," Billy grumbled. "I'll never make a detective, Dan."

Fire streaked from tightening brake shoes as the air checked the forward rush of the freight cars. The long train ground to a jerky halt, and Dan and Billy dropped to the hard packed right of way on the left side of the northbound train. Both welcomed the stop. They stepped cautiously behind a pile of ties.

"Now watch those gondolas ahead," Dan ordered.

The glow from the panting engine was more than enough to reveal anyone leaving the train and passing in front of them. They watched closely. In less than a minute their vigilance was rewarded. They saw Corbin Watson drop down from a gondola and move away from the tracks into the thick woods bordering the railroad. With Dan in the lead, the pair hurried along the side of the train after him at what they believed to be a safe distance. Their running feet slid and hissed in the loose gravel. That gravel was their undoing.

With startling suddenness the scene changed. Watson, aware now that he was being followed, dropped to his knees and faced them. He had gained the security of the woods. Now the enemy's gun spat flame and grim death. Billy stumbled and sprawled headlong; Dan flung himself behind a tree. He had his own gun out— a big automatic, and it too barked and streaked livid fire. Racing bullets bit into the timber and pinged harmlessly against the steel of the freight's gondola. Billy lay perfectly still in the long grass.

Dan's eyes narrowed to calculating slits. He took careful aim as he took in the scene before him. A pale white hand holding an automatic pistol was sneaking around the trunk of Corbin Watson's tree. Dan pulled the trigger—firing twice. There was the blasting roar of the gun and then an agonized shriek of pain. Watson dropped his gun as though it were red hot and stumbled out from behind his shelter. The wounded man screamed again and the sheer horror of the noise made Dan's blood run cold. Watson's cry came again, and it had a hardly-human, eerie quality that made his heart pound madly. The wind was rising with a peculiar moaning which seemed almost human and the rustling of the many leaves added in considerable measure to the uncanny atmosphere. A branch of a tree brushed his cheek and he jumped involuntarily. He was chilled to the bone and shivers were creeping up and down his spine.

Dan fought down the rising fear that choked him and made a quick resolution. Safety depended upon a whirlwind battle, and so Dan went into action. Bending low, like a football player bucking a heavy wall of linemen, he charged through the dark and across the space separating him from the wounded Watson. With one mighty kick he sent the enemy's gun flying into a clump of bushes. Then his doubled fist thrashed out—pounded into the white face of the other man.

Taken off guard, Watson threw up his arms in a vain effort to regain his balance. Warm blood spattered into Dan's determined face. Watson tottered and crashed headlong to the ground. Dan sprawled on top of him and they battled in silent fury, fists flailing in the darkness. They regained their feet and a torment of doubt stormed through Dan's mind. Was Billy Parker alive? Where were the rest of the ghost gang? Why had he been fool enough to drop his own gun?

Dan was waging a hard, scientific battle, carefully aiming blows—crashing into Watson's face again and again with stinging punches. His left found his opponent's midriff time after time. But Watson stayed with him, small, game and as furious as a crippled wildcat. Dan bored in close with both arms beating a merciless tattoo against the other's ribs. He felt Watson weaken and sag. The time had come for him to hurl all of his young strength into a last fierce, finishing attack. He aimed a right hook at the other's jaw—a right hook which he started far down, and which gained momentum as it soared upward. With a jar that rocked Watson on his heels, the savage blow smashed home. Curtains! Corbin Watson swayed crazily; his feet folded under him and he slumped to the ground. There was a low moan; then he was quiet.

The victorious Dan stood over his inert victim for a moment, and then he returned to the spot where Billy lay on the ground. Billy was stirring a little now and his eyes were open. Dan bent anxiously over him.

"Billy—Billy! Are you O.K., pal?"

Billy declared in a weak voice that he was.

"Did any of Watson's bullets nip you, Billy?"

Billy Parker managed to sit up. His head was clearing. "Nope."

"What happened?"

"I wanted to get out of his way and I started to duck for the nearest tree, just as you did. But luck wasn't with me. I tripped on something and fell flat. Everything suddenly went black. What happened to Watson?"

"I knocked him out a second ago. He'll come around in a couple of minutes."

"You've got blood all over you," Billy observed. "Musta been some fight."

"It was, and I have plenty of sore places as souvenirs, but the blood is from Watson's bullet wound. I nicked him in the hand before the battle—made him drop his gun."

"Nice work. Now help a guy up."

Together they surveyed the damage done by Dan's efficient fists. Corbin Watson still slept peacefully where he had fallen.

"I'd hate to get in a free for all with you," Billy told his friend in an awed tone. "You really pounded him, but what do we do with him? That's the present problem."

Suddenly Dan remembered that they were not alone in the night. The fast freight which had carried them from Norfolk still was taking on water two hundred feet away. And at that moment the engineer whistled a highball signal. Dan suddenly had an idea.

"Watson isn't hurt badly and he'll come around

shortly. I know how we can take care of him. Pick up his feet, Billy. We're going to hoist him onto that freight train. When he wakes up, he'll be miles from here—where he can't bother anyone."

Together they carried the unconscious Watson down the long line of cars until they came to an open box car door. The pair boosted their charge inside, then climbed in after him. As the freight started forward, Dan finished binding his recent opponent's hand with his own handkerchief. Billy slipped part of Watson's coat under his head, and then they jumped from the moving train as it gathered speed. The long line of freight cars rolled by and clanked on into the darkness. The lights on the rear of the caboose rapidly receded and became twin crimson dots in the distance.

"When he wakes up, he'll wonder what struck him," Billy chuckled gleefully, "and the train will be moving too fast for him to get off."

They walked back along the track in silence. Crickets sang in the grass beside the rails. The moon refused to come from behind the clouds and the night gently brushed their faces.

"We're going to discover what tripped you up," Dan declared.

They left the railroad again and slowly made

their way through thick underbrush. In five minutes they were back where Billy had tripped and fallen. Billy walked on and after a short search found Watson's gun. Dan was lighting matches and peering inquisitively at the small area illuminated by the flickering light. Suddenly he shouted with joy.

Billy was startled. "What's the matter?"

"Nothing—nothing. Come here—quick!"

Billy was at his side in an instant. Dan lit another match and stooped low. His voice held exciting triumph.

"Here's what you caught your foot on. And no wonder!"

He pointed to a rusty iron rail, half hidden in the grass and then to another.

"You tripped on one rail and banged against its twin," he explained. "We have found the old railroad track leading to the abandoned quarry I told you about! The ties are buried in the ground and the rails are half hidden themselves. See—they've been used recently. These small bushes are broken down and some of the rust has been rubbed off. This track leads from the quarry to the Chicago and Southern main line."

"But where does it connect with the Chicago and Southern main line?"

"That's just what is bothering me. *It doesn't.*"

"What!"

"You heard me. This old, half hidden spur track does not connect with the Chicago and Southern. It once did, but the switch was taken out five years ago when the quarry was finally abandoned."

"But how did the ghost gang transfer the Special from the main line to the quarry track?" Billy queried impatiently.

"Frankly, I don't know, but we'll try to find out."

Groping their way along the twin rails, they followed the tracks to the spot where they disappeared into a pile of gravel fifteen feet from the Chicago and Southern main line.

"I'm convinced that the Midnight Special was transferred to the old spur track right here," Dan said. "Exactly how the trick was done, I can't say, but the answer will probably arrive a little later, as a matter of course. Now let's trace the old tracks to the quarry."

They turned back and carefully made their way along the rusty steel. It was hard going in the darkness. They often stumbled and fell and thorny bushes tore at their clothes.

"This suit I'm wearing looks like something set out on the back porch for the Salvation Army," the irrepressible Billy declared.

It was past midnight and growing colder. Both young men shivered a little as they stumbled along between the rails. They followed the steel through a small clump of trees and over a slight rise, and another thousand feet brought them to a clearing. The moon came from behind the clouds and now shone palely, outlining the gaunt trees that stood silent guard over a shack in the center of the cleared space.

The shack, a tumbledown structure with most of the roof fallen in, was sheltered and half hidden by the sturdy oak trees bordering the clearing. Pale moonlight filtered through the branches of protecting oaks to splash against rough walls.

Dan and Billy left the spur track and stumbled over to the shack through weeds and grass. It had two small windows and a wide front door, like a garage. In the mysterious distance a dog howled and his eerie call was answered by the weird hoot of an owl. Dan shivered involuntarily. It was a lonely night and the ghost gang was at large, perhaps planning yet another train abduction.

Summoning up all their courage and carefully pulling themselves up against the rough wooden walls of the shack, they peered into the interior through the larger of the two grimy windows.

Suddenly they drew back in startled surprise.

The shack in the clearing sheltered a strange secret.

Dan Hyland gave vent to a long, excited whistle.

"Whew!" he exclaimed in a hoarse whisper. "Now we know *why* the good citizens of Skunk Valley are sure that the missing Midnight Special passed through their village early this morning."

CHAPTER XXII

Victory for Three

THE moon slipped beneath another blanketing cloud, and the interior of the shack was no longer visible. But one long look had answered a baffling question. Feeling that they were near the quarry, Dan and Billy left the clearing behind, planning to return later.

They regained the rusted tracks and pushed onward through the chill. About them great trees waved and beckoned with siren limbs. They seemed alone and forlorn in the night. The few stars visible overhead were glitteringly distant and aloof.

Ahead they could make out what appeared to be another clearing. Great oaks were again silhouetted against a black curtain, and they saw the dim outlines of small buildings and shacks. Dan stumbled and nearly fell over a loose cable stretched through the rank grass. He rubbed a bruised shin and tried not to use hard words.

"Watch your step," Billy warned, "and don't tumble into the quarry. I think we have arrived."

"I *know* we have." Dan was gingerly avoiding

the rusted parts of junked machinery which were everywhere on the ground. "Move slowly now."

Cold wind blew in their faces. The desolation seemed complete. They crept to the edge of the quarry hole, gripping the cold jagged bordering stones with numb, sore hands. Once again the moon provided feeble light. Before them, dark water rippled in the bleak night—black wet set against the rocky whiteness of sheer quarry walls. Breathless with interest, Dan and Billy stared out over the secretive pool. Dan pointed out where the old siding came to an end at the edge of the big hole. At the end of those rails the Midnight Special had plunged to a dark watery grave! The explosion of the locomotive boiler had been heard in Kiowa.

"This quarry hole and its slimy water gives me the creeps," Billy confided. "Let's have a look around—elsewhere."

In answer Dan clapped his right hand over Billy's mouth. In an excited whisper he begged his friend to be quiet. They both heard weird sounds—the metallic clanking of chains against hard rock. They were not alone at the old quarry.

The unearthly sound came nearer. Silently, Billy and Dan found shelter behind a large stone. They could now closely watch the activities of others without being seen themselves. A strange

barbaric scene was enacted before their frightened eyes.

Oil lanterns threw bobbing splotches of light
along the rocky path leading from the abandoned
quarry office to the water filled pit. Silent, white
robed figures, bound together with great chains,
emerged from the old office and made their way
along the difficult pathway. The ghostly figures
seemed almost like shrouded monks from the past.
With slow tread they came on down the path
toward the brink of the pit, their binding chains
clanking on the stones. Each white-robed figure
was chained to the man in front of him, and a
great rock had been attached to the last man—a
rock wheeled along on a handtruck after the
silent line by two masked men. The men in white
were marching to their doom.

Dan grasped the terrible meaning of the scene
before him in a fearful instant. The men in the
white shrouds were all prisoners of the ghost
gang. They were about to be drowned wholesale.
Securely bound together and weighted down by
the big rock, they would be forced to jump into
the dark, swirling water of the quarry pool.
Masked men followed the prisoners, but only one
of the gang was armed. The leader, a big heavy
set man dressed in sombre black, brandished a
high powered shot gun. In grim silence, the sil-

ence of death, they were marching to their doom.

Dan and Billy silently stole to a better vantage point, behind another huge protecting rock. They watched the prisoners and the ghost gang with fascinated eyes as the procession halted at the edge of the quarry hole. Below there was icy, cruel water. The victims of the ghost gang waited on the jagged rocks.

The big man with the gun spoke. "When I fire this gun, all of you will leap into the water. The rock will be pushed over the edge at the same instant. It will drag you down—down—down."

The leader laughed and the sound he made was the horrible chortle of a near maniac. Silence met his orders—silence that was complete and terrible.

The exact moment for action had arrived.

Dan Hyland quietly climbed to the top of the protecting rock. He meant to take a desperate chance—alone. He had thrust his gun into the hands of his friend. Billy also had Corbin Watson's gun. Somehow—someway, he was going to save the lives of the ghost gang's prisoners. The sullen members of the gang stood back from the quarry's edge, looking on with barbaric pleasure.

"Get ready to drown yourselves." The insane laugh of the leader rang hideously in the night.

Dan Hyland stood on the top of the rock for

a brief second—then he flung himself through chill air. The entire night world spun crazily and was a topsy-turvy thing as he hurtled feet first into the leader of the ghost gang. Dan saw hard stone rush up at him and he caught a glimpse of startled, half-masked faces. He landed squarely on the leader, and they plunged to the ground together.

Billy Parker was doing his part. "Stand back! All of you!" He leaped from behind the great rock and pointed his two ugly weapons at the masked and astonished ghost gang. Without waiting to be challenged and to give weight to his shouted warning, he blazed away recklessly with both guns. Blinding flame spat from stubby muzzles. Livid, spurting red and blue fire ate at the night and steel bullets scattered through the dark. One of the more venturesome members of the ghost gang screamed with terror and pain and clutched at a wounded arm, then sank to his knees. Billy Parker meant business. He had won his little argument!

Dan and his opponent struggled to their feet, kicking, biting, struggling. Fighting for his own life and for the lives of the prisoners, Dan traded blow for blow as they stumbled into the same rock that had protected the young rescuers a moment before. A heavy fist clipped him behind the ear, leaving a ringing sound and flashing, sparkling colored lights behind his skull. He pumped two hard blows at his foe and they smashed home into pulpy skin. Dan's own lips were split and he had lost his coat; his tattered shirt clung to him in shreds. Billy Parker held back the ghost gang with his menacing guns. Dan fought like a young tiger. The battle raged with savage fierceness. Dan's opponent was big and strong, and he used gutter fighting methods.

The pounding went on with Dan raining blows into his enemy's face. He jabbed home smashing punches that punished his own bleeding fists as well as his opponent. A left and a right found his own face and for a moment he staggered, only to renew his attack a second later. He must win! He must! His future—the Clarion's future, depended upon victory. Billy was successfully holding off the rest of the gang. It was up to him to conquer the leader.

Dan lunged forward with new vigor and put telling force into a last attack. Dan's right shot out and upward, like a vicious piston. It crashed into the masked face with punishing force. Suddenly the battle was finished. His gang leader opponent moaned in pain and pitched to the ground, unconscious. Dan's hard fists and heavy blows had been too much for him.

Dan bent over and tore the mask from the face of the leader. With a cry of triumph he stepped back so that Billy could see. The man on the ground was Con Sheldon!

The desperate battle to save the prisoners of the ghost gang had finished almost before it had begun. Dan and Billy had in ten seconds' time turned the tables on Con Sheldon and his gang. Their days of crime were over. They had temporarily won, only to lose in the end.

The members of the ghost gang were lined up and carefully guarded by Billy Parker while Dan liberated the prisoners. They all proved to be the mail clerks, guards, and baggagemen of the missing train. Slauson, the engineer, and Marston, the old railroad surveyor, were also among the prisoners.

All of the group were glad to be released from their chains. When freed they joyously helped Dan and Billy securely fasten the captured gangsters together with the chains which a moment before had been about themselves. It was a great moment for them and for Dan most of all. He had made good all his promises to the citizens of Norfolk. He knew now where the Special had been dumped; he had captured the gang responsible for the Chicago and Southern robberies and its leader. Tomorrow a special

Extra Edition of the Clarion would shout the story of his victory. Victory at last!

One by one the recent prisoners thanked Dan and Billy in heartfelt words for their life saving assistance.

"We can never thank you enough," said one railway mail clerk. "You saved our lives. The Con Sheldon gang wanted us out of the way, because dead men tell no tales."

"Forget it," Dan replied modestly. "I'm glad Billy and I happened on the scene at just the right moment."

"The loot from the safe in the baggage car and the sacks of registered mail are in the shack where we have been kept prisoners since the robbery. This Sheldon gang robbed the train at their leisure, after they had brought it up here from the main line. Then it was run to the end of the old track and allowed to drop into the water." The speaker was Slauson, the kidnapped engineer. "I was forced to run the train up here from Tower XY blindfolded. They shoved the engine and cars into the water themselves. Old 3011's boiler exploded as she plunged to her wet grave. I thought someone would hear the noise and investigate, especially when the Special didn't show up at Norfolk."

"The boiler explosion *was* heard, as far away

as Kiowa, but no one attached any importance to the noise." Dan grinned. The rescued prisoners gathered about him.

"You see, this man Sheldon was clever. He didn't want the authorities or any other person to discover the real location of the Special, so he directed attention away from this particular section of the country. No one thought about the old stone quarry and its abandoned railroad siding, and I'll explain why."

"I wish you would," old Marston laughed. "How did he direct attention away from the siding and stone quarry?"

"——By building a 'fake Midnight Special' and by running it on the main line almost to Savanna," Dan explained carefully.

"What!" The yell was incredulous. The rescued men crowded around him.

"I mean exactly what I said," Dan continued blandly. "Con Sheldon stole an ordinary gasoline motor track car from the railroad—one of those little cars that chugs and races along the rails carrying track inspectors and section men as passengers.

"Sheldon next installed a complete and powerful public address system on that car—huge loud speaker capable of tremendous volume, a big amplifier, and last but certainly not least, an electric phonograph. You see, Con Sheldon knew that the phonograph companies often provide radio stations with special recordings of sound effects. He obtained a sound effect recording— *a record of a fast train in motion!* On that special record were all the regular train noises: whistle, bell, moving cars, wheels clicking over rail ends, and the staccato bark of the exhaust. Great batteries were installed on the rail car to provide the electricity needed by the amplifier-phonograph. The fake Special now needed only one thing to make it complete—a headlight.

"Con Sheldon next had a locomotive headlight mounted on a mast. He attached the mast to the fake 'train' he had made out of the track jitney. He had the lamp mounted at just the right height to give the proper illusion."

Dan paused in his story to notice that even the gangster prisoners were listening to him with sullen, completely cowed attention. "Before I go on," he said, "I'd like to know how Con Sheldon managed to switch the Special from the main line to the quarry spur without leaving traces of his feat behind. Can you help me there, Marston?"

Forgotten was the dark and the chill early morning. They all eagerly waited for the aged and shaken Marston to speak.

"I *can* help you, Hyland. Sheldon kidnapped me so that I could solve his engineering problems and help him steal the entire train. He wanted to do it as a big practical joke—as a sort of stunt. He wanted to rob the train at leisure, without running the risk of having Lucian Kyle's tiny cameras and microphones tell tales on him afterward, so he planned to rob, dump the train in the quarry, and then do away with the prisoners he was forced to abduct with the train. He even planned another robbery similar to the last one, but you have prevented that. He also enlarged his gang for the train kidnapping and made his headquarters here at the quarry. You might say that Sheldon kidnapped the train as a grand gesture of defiance.

"Con came to my house near the Gosport gravel pit and seized me. I slightly wounded one of his own men. You have captured all of the principal members of the ghost gang. They all came here to the quarry hide-out to watch us drown. We were all to die because Con knew he had been recognized. He planned to take no chances.

"This is how the train was transferred from the main line to the siding: Sheldon bought an ingenious temporary switch from a railroad supply company in New York—a makeshift switch that can be installed and removed in a very short time. He had the old spur lengthened to within a few feet of the main line. He had gravel and ballast ready to support the temporary connection. All was ready. Slauson was kidnapped to pilot the stolen flyer.

"The train was stopped at Tower XY and brought to the point where the switch and temporary track had been laid and connected during the night. I was forced to supervise the track laying operations at the point of a gun. Dave Dempster, the man that the two baggagemen are now guarding and eight members of the ghost gang did the actual work of installation. When the train arrived, the blindfold was taken from Slauson's eyes and he was forced to run the engine and cars over the temporary switch and track at a snail's pace. The train barely crept onto the siding, but it heaved and pitched as if it were going to leave the rails. Then it proceeded slowly up the spur while Dempster and his men removed the switch and extra track and carefully obliterated all traces of the strange transfer. The roadbed was smoothed over and gravel was dumped along the right of way where the switch and rails had been placed. The end of the siding was buried in gravel and sand. They succeeded in making the spot look exactly as it had before.

"The train was robbed here at the quarry after the mail clerks and baggagemen were forced out with tear gas. Then it was run to the end of the siding and plunged into the quarry hole with a roar and a splash. That's the end of my part of the story."

One of the mail clerks began to speak, giving more information. "This place," he told Dan and Billy, "has been completely equipped as a hide-out. There are secret tunnels and caches, and all of the loot taken from the train is hidden here, but the casual visitor, happening to come by, would see no sign of occupation. You were lucky to arrive at the moment when the gang was bringing us out of one of their cleverly constructed hide-aways. We were outfitted in these white shrouds because of Sheldon's crazy ideas of the dramatic. He thought it fitting that we should drown in white. But we're safe, because of your well timed rescue."

"Now I'll finish my part of the explanation," Dan modestly ignored the clerk's praise. "To completely throw suspicion away from the quarry and this neighborhood, Sheldon brought his fake train into use. He ran the track car with its blazing headlight and amplified sound effects from the end of the quarry siding along the main line to a spot beyond Skunk Valley."

He paused for a moment, then went on. "The real train went through Ridgedale and was really seen there. Then its place was taken by the fake train. With its blazing, blinding headlight and with its loud speaker continually blaring out well reproduced and realistic 'train in motion' noises. Con's dummy sounded just like a real train in the dark. The natives of Skunk Valley saw the headlight and they heard a realistic whistle. They heard a clanging bell, the hiss of live steam, the pounding of drivers, the chuff-chuff of an exhaust stack, and the sound of wheels clicking over rail joints. The faked flyer was undoubtedly very realistic. It went through Skunk Valley at the right moment. The villagers reported that the Midnight Special had passed through and directed suspicion away from the section of track between Ridgedale and Skunk Valley. We found the fake train in a shack between here and the main line. Having served its purpose extremely well, it was probably brought back by truck. Police, railroad detectives, reporters, and the curious, wasted time and were decoyed away from the quarry and its siding. The search was concentrated between Skunk Valley and Savanna."

"You have completely solved and explained the mystery of the missing Midnight Special,"

Billy laughed. "Now let's get back to Norfolk. I want to telephone Gargan the big news. It'll be a great scoop! I can see the headlines now. Young Editor finds missing train—*Captures robber gang—Recovers loot—Fulfills promise made to the citizens of Norfolk despite great odds.*"

"Don't lay it on too thick," Dan pleaded.

"I can't say too much," Billy replied. "You're responsible for the solution of the train mystery and the capture of Con Sheldon and his ghost gang, fellow. And you're going to receive the credit you justly deserve. I merely tagged along. You, Dan, turned defeat into victory. You gambled everything on your ability to catch Sheldon and his crowd redhanded and find the train, and you are going to enjoy the fruits of victory."

"Winning out over Sheldon—beating his evil forces is enough for me," Dan said quietly, glancing at the forlorn but now conscious Con.

"You're fine," was his friend's reply. "Now let's wind things up here and get back to town. We'll have to hike to Skunk Valley and wake up somebody." Billy remembered the fake train. "The natives must be pretty dumb—they mistook a headlight and a blaring amplifier for the Midnight Special."

"They believed exactly what Con Sheldon wanted them to," Dan reminded him. "Remember, he fooled us too—just as he planned to do, by directing attention away from the quarry and siding. He knew that anyone interviewing the natives at Ridgedale and Skunk Valley would draw the most obvious conclusion—that the Special had really gone through those two villages, to disappear before arriving at the third, when in reality the stolen train only went through Ridgedale. Sheldon's dupe train seems impossible to you now because you've had a look behind the scenes. Tricks always seem astonishingly simple, after the magician has explained them."

"I suppose you're right. Now let's get out of here."

The prisoners, from the cringing and beaten Con Sheldon down, were herded together in the shack they had been using as a meeting place. Well armed, six rescued mail clerks stayed in the shack to guard them and the recovered loot— cash and mail from the drowned Midnight Special. The rest of the rescued men accompanied Dan and Billy to the main line and into Skunk Valley.

On the way to the main line Dan called a halt so that the rescued mail clerks and baggagemen might view Sheldon's fake train. The queer contraption with its elevated headlight, public address system, horns, and powerful batteries was a grotesque object, but speeding through the night with its headlight glowing and its horns loudly broadcasting train noises, it had been accepted as the real Midnight Special by people in their beds and perhaps only half awake.

At Skunk Valley they met state troopers, who listened to Dan's story in amazement. Five of them immediately left for the quarry to take charge of the prisoners. Three others drove the victory party to Norfolk.

In Norfolk Billy Parker telephoned his exclusive story to the Star, scooping every other newspaper. Dan was the hero of the generous Billy's story. Dan had accomplished everything he had set out to do. The Norfolk Clarion was now ready to enter into the greatest and most successful era of its history. Dan Hyland had won his battle—had won for the Clarion, his own paper. He had justified the faith and confidence of his uncle and George Anderson Gargan. Thousands of words were going out over telegraph wires about him. By noon he would be a hero.

But Dan Hyland did not want to be a hero! He wanted to keep on being just a natural young man with a love for newspaper work—a brilliant young man but a simple and kind one.

Through the early morning hours Dan and Billy and Leslie Wysong worked in the Clarion office on a Victory Edition. At eight o'clock Dan paused from going over damp galley proofs and thought for a moment of the success he had won. Friendly sunshine filled his heart and banished the fears and shadows which had been a part of the night. A clear, cool world stretched away from the Clarion office.

The warm sun shone on Norfolk.

Fortune smiled upon Dan Hyland.

THE END